The *WISE* Handbook

OF MASONRY
AND WATERPROOFING

Material on Waterproofing by

Robert D. Eckhouse

1952
WM. H. WISE & CO., INC.
NEW YORK

Introduction

This volume is divided into two sections. The first (Chapters 1-3), concerns itself with Masonry, Bricklaying, and Masonry projects; the second (Chapters 4 to 12, incl.) covers Waterproofing and Dampproofing. More than 200 illustrations accompany the text.

The aim of the first section (Masonry) is to assist the home handyman in both speeding up needed concrete and brick construction and to produce quality results. Proportioning concrete the modern way is one of the many helpful points covered in Chapter 1, along with the latest information on mixing, placing, finishing and curing concrete. In addition, colored concrete and unusual surface finishes are also discussed. The information is practical having been developed and tested in the laboratories of the Portland Cement Association.

Following these basic fundamentals, Chapter 3 sets forth detailed instructions for the construction of such masonry projects as a concrete baseball home plate, bench, bicycle stand, curbs, foundations, garage, shuffleboard court, and numerous others.

The major section, or final two-thirds, of the volume is devoted to an exhaustive treatment of Waterproofing and Dampproofing.

Yearly, millions of dollars are spent on materials and labor in an effort to correct wet cellars, walls, and ceilings. Unfortunately, most of the money is wasted. Natural impulse dictates making repairs where the stains appear, but the leakage then shifts and shows up again at some other spot.

The only way that dampness can be effectively stopped is to ferret out the cause or source of the trouble. Throughout Chapters 4 to 12, inclusive, this point is emphasized repeatedly, and if the suggestions made therein are followed carefully the source of the trouble can be determined and corrected. However, where the cause cannot be found it is advisable to seek the assistance of a waterproofing engineer before trying to make the repair yourself.

Once you are certain as to why water leaks into your home you can proceed with the repair work as described in the second section of this volume. It is extremely important, though, to use reliable waterproofing products. Thousands of homeowners are being misled and disillusioned by alleged cure-alls which are purchased on the basis of exaggerated claims. Beware of these false products. They are a waste of time and money. Reliable waterproofers are available on the market which produce satisfactory results if used in accordance with the manufacturer's instructions.

The possibility of water penetrating your home exists whether you live in an old or new house. While most new dwellings are built with all the ordinary precautions necessary for dryness, the introduction of new electrical appliances and the well insulated design of most new homes, frequently contribute to "steamed up" windows and internal leaking due only to condensation. Obviously, such a condition must be corrected quite differently from ordinary leakage.

Remember, there are two important considerations with regard to waterproofing. The first is how to remedy a water situation when it develops. The second requires an acceptance of the fact that proper care and maintenance of the home must include precautions which will prevent water penetration.

To those of you who unfortunately are tormented with damp cellars, leaky roofs, or other annoyances, the latter two-thirds of this volume offer practical ideas and recommendations as to corrective measures. Other homeowners, who luckily have not yet encountered any water problems, are warned to be on guard and to follow the suggestions covering maintenance methods to insure dryness.

A dry house is within the reach of every house owner. It affords wholesome, sanitary living conditions, promotes comfort and health, and lengthens the life and value of the house and furnishings. A house free of dampness and water problems is not an accident; it must be made that way and kept that way. A grasp of the fundamentals detailed herein is all the home handyman needs to achieve this goal for himself and his family.

ACKNOWLEDGEMENTS: We wish to take this opportunity to express our thanks and appreciation for the assistance and information received from the Portland Cement Association, Chicago, Illinois, and the Anti-Hydro Waterproofing Company, Newark, N. J. We wish also to express our thanks to the illustrators of this book: Carl T. Sigman; William Ward, Jr.; Fergus Retrum; William A. Patrick; Carl R. Kinscherf; William Bolin; Elaine White; Jane Karl; Lois Brand.

CONTENTS

v

3. MASONRY PROJECTS — *Continued*

4. WATER AND DAMPNESS 80

5. CONDENSATION 97

6. TOOLS AND MATERIALS FOR WATERPROOFING 112

10. SUPERSTRUCTURE — *Continued*

11. THE ROOF 218

12. THE BATHROOM AND KITCHEN; THE ATTIC 234

The _WISE_ Handbook
OF MASONRY
AND WATERPROOFING

CHAPTER 1

FACTS ABOUT CONCRETE

What It Is

Concrete consists of a mass of fine and coarse materials, known as *aggregates,* which are surrounded and held together by hardened portland cement paste. The concrete is strong if the paste is strong and the aggregates durable. The concrete is watertight if the paste is watertight. The concrete is durable if the paste and aggregates are durable.

When the materials for concrete are first mixed together, the cement and water form a paste. This paste then surrounds the particles of aggregate and holds them together to form concrete (Fig. 1). The latter is in a plastic condition, initially, following which a chemical action takes place between the cement and water causing the paste to harden.

If strong concrete is desired, the paste must have a high strength when hardened. If too much water is added during mixing, the paste becomes thin or diluted and will be weak when it hardens. Such a paste will not hold the particles of aggregate firmly together. As a result, the concrete will be weak because the pieces of aggregate will be held together only partially. Conversely, cement paste which has good holding qualities will hold the particles of aggregate firmly together to form strong concrete. Thus the water and cement are the important ingredients in a concrete mixture.

SELECTION OF MATERIALS

Choosing suitable materials is the first step in making concrete that is to be strong, durable and watertight. The qualities of portland cement, mixing water and aggregates which make them suitable for use in a concrete mixture follow:

Portland Cement

Note: portland refers to a type of cement and not to the name of a brand.

Type I—For use in general concrete construction when the special properties specified for Types II, III, IV and V are not required.

Type II—For use in general concrete construction exposed to moderate sulfate action, or where moderate heat of hydration is required.

Type III — For use when high early strength is required.

Type IV—For use when a low heat of hydration is required.

Type V—For use when high sulfate resistance is required.

Note: Cements conforming to the requirements for Types IV and V are not usually carried in stock. Before specifying their use, purchasers should determine whether these types can be made available.

Mixing Water

Generally speaking, only water that is fit to drink is suitable for mixing cement. Water that is clean and free from oil, alkali, or acid is particularly suitable.

Aggregates

Aggregates usually are divided into fine and coarse. Sand (Fig. 2) is the most common form of fine aggregate, and pebbles, crushed stone, or crushed slag the most common forms of coarse aggregate. Sand or other fine aggregate includes all particles from very fine (exclusive of dust) up to those which will pass through a screen with meshes ¼ inch square. Coarse aggregate (Fig. 3) includes pebbles, crushed stone, or crushed slag ranging from ¼ to 1½ inches or larger.

The largest size of coarse aggregate to use is governed by the nature of the work. Aggregate up to 1½ inches or more in size may be used in a thick foundation wall or heavy footing, while in thin slabs or walls the largest pieces of aggregate should never exceed one-third the thickness of the concrete being placed.

As a general rule aggregates which are sound, hard, and durable are best suited for use in concrete. Aggregates which are soft and flaky, and which will wear away rapidly through exposure are unsatisfactory. In addition to being sound, hard, and durable, the best aggregates are clean and free from fine dust, loam, clay, or vegetable matter. Concrete made with dirty aggregates hardens slowly, and may never harden enough to serve its purpose.

Well-graded fine aggregate, in which the particles are not all fine or all coarse, but vary from fine up to those particles which will just pass a screen with meshes ¼ inch square, is recommended. If the sand is well graded, the finer particles fill the voids between the larger particles,

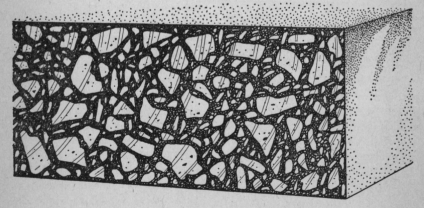

Fig. I. Photograph showing a piece of concrete which has been sawed in two. As is characteristic of good concrete, the pieces of aggregate are held together by the cement paste and *each piece* is completely coated with cement paste.

Fig. 2. Sample of well-graded sand before and after it has been separated into various sizes. Particles vary from fine up to ¼ inch, the width of strips indicating amounts of each size. This is good sand for concrete work. For good workability, at least 10 per cent should pass a 50-mesh sieve.

resulting in the most economical use of cement paste in filling the voids and binding the aggregate together.

Coarse aggregate is well graded when the particles range from ¼-inch up to the largest that can be used for the particular project.

The natural mixture of fine and coarse aggregates, as taken from a gravel bank or crusher, seldom is suitable for concrete unless first screened to separate the fine material from the coarse, and then recombined in the correct proportion for the class of concrete desired. Most gravel banks contain either more sand or more coarse material than is desirable, while bank-run material contains too much sand.

PROPORTIONING CONCRETE

It is an easy matter to proportion concrete by methods which control the *total amount* of water that is mixed with each sack of cement, and thus control the quality of the concrete. The first step is to determine the quality of cement paste required for the particular job.

Recommended qualities of concrete for various classes of work are listed in the accompanying Table which is the guide to proportioning concrete materials according to the *total amount* of water required to mix with each sack of cement. The Table is based on the following facts:

(1) A cement paste made in a proportion of not more than 5 gallons of water to one sack of cement will produce satisfactory concrete for work subjected to severe wear, weather, or weak acid and alkali solutions. Jobs that require this kind of concrete include colored topping for sidewalks, tennis courts, and floors, in addition to plain topping for all two-course work.

RECOMMENDED PROPORTIONS OF WATER TO CEMENT AND SUGGESTED TRIAL MIXES

KINDS OF WORK	Add U. S. Gal. of Water to Each Sack Batch If Sand Is			Suggested Mixture for Trial Batch			Materials per cu. yd. of Concrete*		
	Very Wet	Wet	Damp	Cement Sacks	Fine Cu. Ft.	Coarse Cu. Ft.	Cement Sacks	Fine Cu. Ft.	Coarse Cu. Ft.

5-GALLON PASTE FOR CONCRETE SUBJECTED TO SEVERE WEAR, WEATHER OR WEAK ACID AND ALKALI SOLUTIONS

KINDS OF WORK	Very Wet	Wet	Damp	Cement Sacks	Fine Cu. Ft.	Coarse Cu. Ft.	Cement Sacks	Fine Cu. Ft.	Coarse Cu. Ft.
Colored or plain topping for heavy wearing surfaces as in industrial plants and all other two-course work such as pavements, walks, tennis courts, residence floors, etc.	4¼	Average Sand 4½	4¾	1	1	1¾	10	10	17

Maximum size Aggregate ⅜″

Colored or plain topping...									
One-course industrial, creamery and dairy plant floors and all other concrete in contact with weak acid or alkali solutions.	3¾	4	4½	1	1¾	2	8	14	16

Maximum size Aggregate ¾″

6-GALLON PASTE FOR CONCRETE TO BE WATERTIGHT OR SUBJECTED TO MODERATE WEAR AND WEATHER

KINDS OF WORK	Very Wet	Wet	Damp	Cement Sacks	Fine Cu. Ft.	Coarse Cu. Ft.	Cement Sacks	Fine Cu. Ft.	Coarse Cu. Ft.
Watertight floors such as industrial plant, basement, dairy barn, etc. Watertight foundations. Concrete subjected to moderate wear or frost action such as driveways, walks, tennis courts, etc. All watertight concrete for swimming and wading pools, septic tanks, storage tanks, etc. All base course work such as floors, walks, drives, etc. All reinforced concrete structural beams, columns, slabs, residence floors, etc.	4¼	Average Sand 5	5½	1	2¼	3	6¼	14	19

Maximum size Aggregate 1½″

7-GALLON PASTE FOR CONCRETE NOT SUBJECTED TO WEAR, WEATHER OR WATER

KINDS OF WORK	Very Wet	Wet	Damp	Cement Sacks	Fine Cu. Ft.	Coarse Cu. Ft.	Cement Sacks	Fine Cu. Ft.	Coarse Cu. Ft.
Foundation walls, footings, mass concrete, etc., not subjected to weather, water pressure or other exposure.	4¾	Average Sand 5½	6¼	1	2¾	4	5	14	20

Maximum size Aggregate 1½″

*Quantities are estimated on wet aggregates using suggested trial mixes and medium consistencies — quantities will vary according to the grading of aggregate and the workability desired.

It may be necessary to use a richer paste than is shown in the table because the concrete may be subjected to more severe conditions than are usual for a structure of that type. For example, a swimming pool ordinarily is made with a 6-gallon paste. However, the pool may be built in a place where soil water is strongly alkaline in which case a 5-gallon paste is required.

(2) A 6-gallon paste produces concrete which is watertight and is satisfactory when subjected to moderate wear and weather. Watertight floors, foundation walls, driveways, sidewalks, and swimming pools are types of work which require concrete of this quality.

(3) A 7-gallon paste will produce concrete which is suitable for use where it will not be subjected to wear, weather, or water pressure. This quality is satisfactory for use in footings and other mass concrete.

Effect of Moisture in Sand

Having selected the *total amount* of water—5, 6, or 7 gallons—to be used with each sack of cement to make a paste of the quality desired, it is necessary to take into account the amount of water carried by the fine aggregate—sand, and similar materials. The amount carried by

coarse aggregate is generally negligible.

Thus the Proportioning Table gives the recommended proportions of water to cement for use in one-sack batches made with sand that is *damp, wet,* or *very wet,* the amounts being based on suggested trial proportions of aggregates of the maximum sizes listed. The reason less water is added at the mixer when sand is *damp, wet,* or *very wet* than when it is *dry,* is that the moisture carried by sand is free to react with the cement in forming the cement paste. Therefore, it is necessary to consider this moisture as part of the mixing water. This was done in compiling the columns, *Very Wet, Wet,* and *Damp,* in the Proportioning Table.

Dry sand is that which is "air dry" —that is, material which is as dry as it would be if it were spread out in a thin layer and dried in the sun or

Fig. 3. This is how a well-graded coarse aggregate appears before and after being separated into three sizes. Reading from left to right, in the separated aggregate, 1/2 to 3/8-inch size, 3/8 to 3/4-inch size, and 3/4 to 1 1/2-inch size. Note how smaller pieces fit in between larger ones in the mixed aggregate.

Fig. 4A View showing stiff, medium, and sloppy mixtures of concrete.

warm air. Such sand, which flows freely, seldom is available for concrete work.

Damp sand is that which feels slightly damp to the touch, but which leaves very little moisture on the hands. It usually contains about ¼ gallon of water per cubic foot.

Wet sand, usually available on most jobs, feels wet and leaves a little moisture on the hands after being handled. It contains about ½ gallon of water per cubic foot.

Very wet sand is dripping wet when delivered and leaves more moisture on the hands than wet sand. It carries about ¾ gallon of water per cubic foot.

Fine sand usually carries more water than coarse sand although from appearance both might seem to be equally wet. Thus when fine sand is used, the quantities of water shown in the Proportioning Table should be reduced about ¼ gallon for damp sand, and about ½ gallon for wet and very wet sand.

Measuring Moisture in Sand

One can determine whether sand is *damp, wet,* or *very wet* once one becomes familiar with the appearance and feel of materials in these conditions.

To become familiar with the appearance and feel of *damp, wet,* or *very wet* sand, fill a clean cement sack about two-thirds full with sand, spread in a thin layer on a clean, dry floor inside a building and let it dry. Stir the sand until all surface moisture disappears and the sand flows freely.

Now measure out three gallons of this dry sand, placing one gallon in each of three pans, and using a prescription bottle as a measure, add 5 ounces of water to one pile, 12 ounces to another, and 20 ounces to the third, mixing each thoroughly.

The pile containing 5 ounces of water is typical of what is known as *damp* sand; that containing 12 ounces as *wet* sand, and the one with 20 as *very wet*. Study and compare the appearance and feel of these piles until the difference is clear to you. For most jobs the condition of sand should be *wet*.

Whenever sand is obtained from a different source of supply, where it may be finer or coarser, repeat the "wetting" test to determine its dampness.

It is important to be able to judge whether sand is *damp, wet,* or *very wet* in order to know how much water to deduct for that carried by

Fig. 4B. A concrete mixture in which there is not sufficient cement-sand mortar to fill spaces between coarse aggregate. Such a mixture will be hard to work and will result in rough, honeycombed surfaces.

the sand. Sand containing 2 per cent moisture carries about ¼ gallon of water per cubic foot; 4 per cent, ½ gallon; 6 per cent, ¾ gallon; 8 per cent, 1 gallon, and 10 per cent, 1¼ gallons per cubic foot.

Proportioning Materials

After the sand to be used has been classified, the Proportioning Table may be referred to in determining the trial proportion for any particular job. If, for example, one desires to determine the proper proportion of materials for building a concrete swimming pool the Proportioning Table specifies a 6-gallon paste. However, for the trial batch, 1:2¼:3, made with *damp* sand, only 5½ gallons of water are added because approximately ½ gallon is contained in the 2¼ cubic feet of sand. With *wet* sand only 5 gallons are added. With *very wet* sand only 4¼ gallons are added.

When you make a trial batch, place one sack of cement, 2¼ cubic feet of sand, and 3 cubic feet of coarse aggregate in the mixer, and add the correct amount of water depending upon the condition of the aggregates. For a swimming pool, using *wet* aggregates, this amount is 5 gallons. This mixture is the *trial* batch, and by noting how it handles and places you will know whether to continue using this *trial proportion* in the remaining batches.

If the concrete in the trial batch is a smooth, plastic, workable mass that will place and finish well, the correct proportion for the job has been determined. Judge it by working the concrete with a shovel or a trowel. The concrete should be stiff enough to stick together, yet not dry enough to be crumbly. On the other hand, if the concrete is thin enough to run, it is not suitable for use. The best mixture is mushy but not soupy (Fig. 4A).

Concrete that places and finishes readily is known as workable concrete. In it there is sufficient cement paste to bind the pieces of aggregate together so they will not separate when the material is transported to or placed in the forms. There also is sufficient cement paste and sand to give good, smooth surfaces free from rough spots, called *honeycombing*. In other words, there is just enough cement paste to fill completely the spaces between the particles of aggregate, and insure a smooth, plastic mix that finishes easily.

Correcting Trial Mixture

If you find the trial mixture is not workable, change the amounts of aggregate used in the concrete but do not change the quantity of water.

Fig. 4C. A mixture in which there is an excess of cement-sand mortar. While such concrete is plastic and workable and will have smooth surfaces, the yield will be low. Such concrete is likely to be porous.

For example, the trial batch of 1 part cement to 2¼ parts sand and 3 parts coarse aggregate (1:2¼:3) mix may be too stiff, too mushy, or may lack smoothness and workability (Fig. 4B). Each of these conditions can be corrected by changing the amounts of aggregate in the mix.

If the trial proportion gives a mixture that is too mushy (Fig. 4C), add small amounts of sand and coarse aggregate in the proportion of 2¼ parts sand and 3 parts coarse aggregate until the right workability (Fig. 4D) is obtained.

If the concrete is too stiff and appears crumbly, succeeding batches are mixed with less aggregates. Usually slightly less coarse material will give the required workability. Ordinarily, the first batch mixed will be somewhat stiffer than the second or third batch as some of the water in the first batch is used in wetting the mixer. Thus if the first batch is only slightly too stiff, it is best not to make any changes in the proportion and amounts of aggregate until after the second and third batches are run through.

Making Economical Concrete

You'll naturally want as much concrete as possible from each sack of cement; thus, the more aggregate mixed with the cement paste, the more concrete you produce. The stiff mix contains the largest amount of aggregate and is ordinarily the most economical from the standpoint of materials. It is, therefore, to one's advantage to use mixes that are as stiff as can be placed readily.

It is poor economy, however, to place a mix that is so stiff that it requires an excessive amount of labor for tamping and spading. What is saved in materials is lost in time and labor. More important, of course, is the danger of getting porous or honeycombed concrete which will readily disintegrate under the action of the weather. It is desirable, then, to select that combination of sand and coarse aggregate that will produce the largest amount of plastic workable concrete from a given amount of paste. Experience has shown that for average sand and coarse aggregate on the average jobs, this proportion is approximately 40 per cent sand and 60 per cent coarse aggregate. Generally, a slightly oversanded mix is the most satisfactory.

Proportioning Fine and Coarse Aggregates

The following recommendations will prove helpful in determining the best proportion of sand to coarse aggregate, these figures being based on materials in *wet* condition as they are found on most jobs:

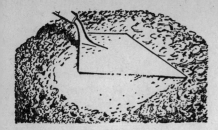

Fig. 4D. A concrete mixture which contains correct mixture of cement-sand mortar. With light troweling all spaces between coarse aggregate are filled with mortar. Note appearance on edges of pile. This is good, workable concrete that will give maximum yield with a given amount of cement paste.

For coarse aggregate ranging from ¼ inch up to 1½ inches, use approximately 40 per cent sand and 60 per cent coarse aggregate.

For coarse aggregate from ¼ inch up to ¾ inch, use about 50 per cent sand and 50 percent coarse aggregate.

The suggested proportions given in the Proportioning Table are for use only in trial batches. Each of these proportions probably will have to be corrected to get the best yield and the desired workability. For foundations, footings, walls, pavements, and work of like character, the stiff consistency is recommended; medium mix is suitable for floors, slabs, beams, and similar work, while sloppy mix is unsuitable for most types of concrete.

MIXING CONCRETE

Accurate measurement of all materials is necessary to insure production of uniform batches of concrete

of the quality desired. The best way to make certain of this is to use weighing or measuring equipment that is designed to give accurate measurements at all times.

Measuring Aggregates

When measuring is done with a shovel, one should check the number of shovelsful he takes in handling exactly one cubic foot of material. Do this easily by counting the number of shovelsful of each material required to fill a cubic foot box, or a cement sack which holds 1 cubic foot.

If measuring is done with a wheelbarrow, it should be marked on the inside for 1 cubic foot, 2 cubic feet, etc. This marking can be done by dumping a cubic-foot box or a cement sack full of material in the barrow, leveling and making a mark at that level. This can be repeated with another cubic foot of material, etc., until the barrow is calibrated.

The most accurate method of measuring, of course, is by weight. On large jobs, platform scales are used with a few shovelsful added or removed in adjustment. Not only is this method more nearly accurate, producing uniformity from batch to batch, but also it is easily adjusted for necessary changes in proportions and completely eliminates the problem of correcting for bulking of sand.

Measuring Water

In using the modern method of proportioning—that of adding a definite amount of water to each sack of cement—it is necessary to maintain accurate measurement of mixing water throughout the job. For large jobs, many concrete mixers are now equipped with tanks and measuring devices which give satisfactory results when properly used. These measuring devices can be set to deliver any number of gallons of water in the mixer drum as specified. An ordinary 12-quart galvanized pail, marked off in gallons, one-half gallons, and one-quarter gallons, is used for measuring water in the absence of measuring devices. A recommended practice for measuring water from a barrel is to keep a pail exclusively for this purpose by the barrel.

Time of Mixing

With a batch-type machine mixer, it is recommended that mixing continue for at least one minute after all materials, including water, are placed in the mixer drum. When every piece of aggregate is completely coated with cement paste, the concrete is well mixed, and more uniform concrete is obtained.

Mixing Improves Workability

Thorough mixing also affords improved workability which reduces the labor required in placing and permits the use of slightly larger quantities of aggregate with a given proportion of cement and water. Contractors find that another advantage of thorough mixing (preferably two minutes) is that it assists in securing watertight concrete.

Small changes in the speed of the mixer have little effect because thoroughness of mixing is governed largely by the time of mixing, and not the rate of rotation of the mixer drum. Loading the mixer above its rated capacity is not recommended as such overloading prevents thorough mixing.

PLACING CONCRETE

The method used to transport concrete from the mixer to the forms depends on job conditions. On small projects wheelbarrows are usual, while on large jobs buggies and chutes are commonly used.

When using barrows or buggies, care is required to prevent segregation (pieces of aggregate separating out) as the concrete is being moved. Segregation is likely to occur when the concrete is handled over rough ground or runways. A rather stiff consistency usually is required to prevent segregation.

Depositing Concrete in Forms

The best practice is to place the concrete in the forms as quickly as possible, and in no event later than 45 minutes after mixing. Before doing so, all debris and, in cold weather, ice are removed from the forms. Following this, the forms are thoroughly wetted (except in freezing weather) or oiled.

Concrete is deposited in level layers, usually not more than 6 inches deep. As it is placed it is tamped and spaded just enough to settle it thoroughly and produce a dense mass. Working the concrete next to the forms insures an even, dense surface.

Fig. 5. Runways built entirely around forms for foundation wall permit placing concrete where needed rather than to deposit it at a few points and drag or cause it to flow where it is to be used. Keeping concrete level in forms prevents segregation and honeycombing.

If the mixture becomes sloppy as the forms are filled due to water being forced out of the lower layers of concrete, use stiffer mixtures.

At the end of a day's run, or where the work has to stop long enough for the concrete to begin to harden, the top surface is roughened just before it hardens so as to remove laitance or scum and provide a good bonding surface for the next layer of concrete. Just before resuming concreting, the roughened surface is cleaned and then brushed with a cement-water paste of a thick, creamy consistency. This paste is applied in a thick brush coat just a few feet ahead of the concreting operation so that it does not have a chance to dry.

Unless care is used in providing a bond between different layers of con-crete, there is danger of seams developing that will cause leakage. This precaution to get a good bond between different layers of concrete is very important wherever the concrete construction is to be watertight.

Preventing Segregation in Forms

It is just as important to prevent segregation in the forms as it is when transporting the concrete from the mixer to the forms. It is good practice to deposit concrete in the forms where it is to be used rather than to place it at a few points and drag it or cause it to flow where needed. Depositing the concrete uniformly around the forms prevents segregation and honeycombing (Fig. 5).

With thoroughly mixed concrete delivered at proper consistency and without segregation, placing of concrete is made easy; but even in this case further care is required to see that the material flows properly into the corners and angles of forms and, in reinforced work, around the reinforcement (Fig. 6).

Placing Concrete by Vibration

Vibration has many advantages as a means for placing concrete. The modern high-frequency concrete vibrators make it possible to place mixtures economically. For example, concrete of a stiff consistency can be readily placed by vibration in forms containing closely spaced reinforcements, which would require a medium consistency with hand-placing. Vibration not only permits the use of stiffer mixes but also permits using a smaller proportion of sand to coarse aggregate, both reducing the amount of mixing water.

Fig. 6. In reinforced concrete work it is necessary to place concrete around and under all reinforcement. On this floor job, the workman is rodding the concrete so that reinforcement will be completely embedded.

FINISHING CONCRETE

Troweling

Smooth finishes are produced with a steel trowel, care being taken to prevent too early troweling or excessive troweling. This care is required because troweling too soon or too much is likely to result in surfaces that will dust or which will develop numerous fine cracks called *hair checks*. These can be avoided by proper finishing to produce surfaces that will be dense, smooth, and which will prove durable in service.

An important factor in producing satisfactory surfaces is the *time of final finishing*. The best practice is to allow the concrete to stand until it is quite stiff but is still workable. Then the steel trowel compacts the concrete and produces a dense surface. When the mixture is quite stiff, cement and fine material are not drawn to the surface under the action of the trowel. Consequently such finishes are free from objectionable dusting and hair checking.

The concrete is struck off carefully just after it is placed in the forms. This removes all humps and hollows leaving a true, even surface for the final troweling operation.

Use of Wood Float

For sidewalks, driveways, and some floors, an even, yet gritty, non-slippery surface often is desired. When a finish of this type is required, final finishing is done with a wood float instead of a steel trowel (Fig 7). Final finishing is delayed until the surface has become quite stiff. The finish produced with a wood float is commonly described as a "sidewalk" finish.

Mechanical Floating

Wear resistance of concrete floors can be improved by using concrete mixes with a low water content and by increasing the amount of coarse aggregate. In placing and floating concrete for industrial and colored floors, a mechanical power float will work stiff concrete mixes containing coarse aggregates which are too harsh for hand floating.

Belt Finishing

On driveways, pavements, and similar work, concrete contractors produce final finish with a belt of wood, canvas or rubber, not less than 6 nor more than 12 inches wide, and at least 2 feet longer than the width of the slab being finished. This is laid on the surface of the concrete immediately after the wood float has been used.

Removing Surface Water

It is best to avoid surface water in the first place. However, when there is a small amount present, the recommended practice is to allow it to evaporate before finishing. If there is considerable water, it is removed with a broom, belt, float, or by other convenient means. It is never good practice to sprinkle dry cement, or a mixture of cement and fine aggregate, on concrete to take up surface water. Such fine materials form a layer on the surface that is likely to dust or hair check when the concrete hardens.

CURING CONCRETE

After choosing suitable materials, proportioning and mixing them according to recommended practice,

Fig. 7. An important operation where an even finish is desired is the use of the long float to remove marks left by the short float.

and properly placing and finishing, the next step in making watertight, durable, strong concrete is to provide proper curing conditions. As previously explained, concrete hardens because of a chemical reaction between portland cement and water. This process continues so long as temperatures are favorable and moisture is present to hydrate the cement.

Effect of Moisture

The desirable properties of concrete — watertightness, durability, and strength — increase with age so long as moisture is present and favorable temperatures prevail. The increase is very rapid during the first week, gradually becoming slower, but continuing over a period of months and even years. The gain in strength during the first week is approximately as great as that during the succeeding 3 months. Once concrete has become thoroughly dry, there is no further gain, unless, at some later date, moist curing is resumed. For this reason, it is especially important to protect concrete from drying or chilling immediately after it is placed.

Effect of Temperature

The most favorable temperatures for curing concrete are from 70 to 80 degrees. At higher temperatures hardening takes place more rapidly unless special precautions are taken to prevent drying. As the temperature is lowered below 70 degrees, the rate of hardening decreases until at 33 degrees (just above freezing) it takes more than 3 times as long to

develop a given strength as it does at 70. No gain whatever can be expected while concrete is frozen, but hardening will be resumed after it is thawed provided suitable curing is applied. Freezing within the first 24 hours is almost certain to result in permanent injury to the concrete.

Curing Increases Watertightness

Thorough moist curing is one of the most important steps in producing watertight concrete. As the cement paste in concrete hardens, new solid material is formed by the combination of the water and cement. This results in more completely filling the spaces between the original particles of cement and sand through which water might otherwise pass. Failure to properly cure concrete which is expected to be watertight does as much damage as leaving out a considerable part of the cement.

Curing Prevents Dusting and Checking

For floors, sidewalks, and other surfaces which must have high resistance to wear, moist curing, especially during the first few days, is absolutely necessary. Naturally, if concrete is not cured, the surface dries first, often within but a few hours after finishing and before hardening is well started. Soon after the surface is put in use, the sand and cement grains begin to dust off and the surface shows signs of wear. Too rapid drying also causes the surface to shrink more than the slab, and checks or pattern cracks are formed.

Both dusting and checking can be prevented or greatly reduced by proper moist curing.

Methods of Curing

Wet burlap, canvas, sand, or straw coverings are often used to protect newly placed concrete. The covering is placed as soon as it can be done without marring the surface, care being taken to keep the covering continuously wet by sprinkling. When a cover is not used, wetting of the concrete is begun soon after finishing.

Floor finishes and the top course of all two-course work require careful attention as moisture is lost not only by evaporation but some may be drawn out by the base course.

Ponding is a good method of curing for flat surfaces, such as floors and pavements. With this method, the surface to be cured is surrounded by small earth dikes and then kept flooded with water for the desired period, usually not less than 5 days.

Another method suitable for curing concrete is a thin membrane seal coat which prevents rapid evaporation of the mixing water needed for proper hydration of the cement. These coatings are sprayed on in 1 or 2 coats immediately after the free water has disappeared from the concrete surface. Both black and transparent coatings are available.

Heavy paper impregnated with asphalt is also used for curing floors and other horizontal surfaces. This is placed as soon as possible without marring the surface. All seams are lapped and sealed with tape to pro-

vide a waterproof covering. The floor finish is also protected from dirt and debris resulting from other building operations.

Walls and other vertical surfaces can be protected by leaving the forms in place temporarily (Fig. 8), or by hanging canvas or burlap over them. Such coverings are kept constantly moist by sprinkling. Curing should continue for at least 5 days, and for longer periods when it is practical to do so.

COLORED CONCRETE

The following recommendations for producing colored concrete are based on tests both in the field and the laboratory and, if carefully observed, should result in thoroughly satisfactory work.

Pigments

A pigment suitable for use in concrete must fulfill the following requirements:

(1) It must be durable under exposure to sunlight and weather.

(2) It must produce intense color.

(3) It must be of such composition that it will not react chemically with the cement to the detriment of either cement or color.

The foregoing requirements are best fulfilled with mineral oxide pigments. Other pigments, such as organic dyes, have a tendency to fade and many reduce the strength of concrete. There are two kinds of mineral oxides available that are satisfactory —natural oxides that come direct

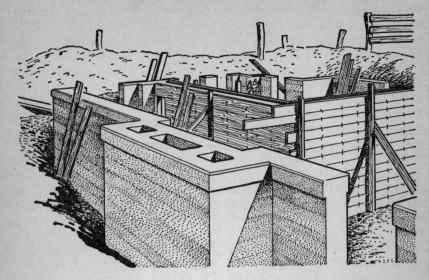

Fig. 8. Formwork left in place on interior wall to assist in proper curing. Forms have been stripped from wall in foreground.

from the mines, and manufactured pigments which are prepared especially for concrete work. Ordinarily, natural mineral pigments cost less per pound than manufactured pigments and may be used where dull colors are satisfactory. However, where bright colors are desired, manufactured pigments produce best results. To get a given amount of color, more of the natural pigment is required than the manufactured pigment. It frequently happens that the smaller amount of high-priced, manufactured pigment actually produces the desired results at a lower cost.

The following recommendations will serve as a guide in determining proper pigments for use in securing the colors listed:

Buff, Yellow or Red—Iron Oxide Pigments.

Green — Chromium Oxide Pigments.

Blue—Cobalt Blue or Ultramarine Blue.

Brown—Iron Oxide or Iron and Manganese Oxide Pigments.

Gray, Slate and Black—Iron Oxide or Manganese Dioxide Pigments.

The color which is produced in concrete is determined primarily by the proportion of pigment to cement and not by the proportion of pigment to cubic feet of mortar or concrete. Because of this, modern color specifications give the weight of pigment to be used per sack of cement.

It has been found that pigments may be safely used in amounts up to 10 per cent of the weight of the cement—that is, 9 pounds of pigment per sack (94 pounds) of cement. These limits may be exceeded with some pigments and under certain conditions. In such cases the manufacturer's directions should be followed.

The aggregates used in making colored concrete should be as near the color of the mortar as possible. If such aggregates are not available, light colored, semi-transparent aggregates will give best results.

With high grade pigments the amount recommended as a maximum —10 per cent of the weight of the cement—will usually produce deep shades of color. Lighter shades are obtained by using less pigment, and variations of color or shades by mixing two or more pigments.

To obtain maximum clearness and brightness in colored finishes, white portland cement should be used. White finishes are obtained by using white portland cement and light colored aggregates.

Quality of Pigments

Mineral pigments vary considerably in coloring values. Most archi-

tects and builders depend upon the reputation of the manufacturer of pigments for assurance that the quality of the material is satisfactory for concrete work. In general, the finer a pigment is ground the greater is its coloring ability and the less required.

Mixing Pigment and Cement

In producing high quality colored concrete (Fig. 9), the pigment and cement are mixed together before they are delivered on the job. Thorough mixing, which is hard to accomplish on the job, is essential because this helps to insure uniform color in the finished work. Likewise, pigments do not penetrate the particles of cement, as do dyes in coloring cloth. Instead, the pigment forms a coating around the particles, making thorough mixing necessary.

Most contractors prefer to mix pigment and cement in a color mixer used only for this purpose. This is done away from the job inside a building, the accurately weighed quantity of pigment being added to each sack of cement and then re-sacked for transporting to the work being done. Mixing should continue for at least 10 minutes when a color mixer is used.

Placing Colored Concrete

Colored concrete may be placed by any one of three recommended methods—two-course, delayed two-course, or one-course method.

Two-Course Method

This method, in which colored topping is placed before the base course

Fig. 9. An unusually attractive colored concrete sidewalk in which the color design is made to conform to the architectural treatment of the building.

Fig. 10. Concrete topping made with 5 gallons of water per sack of cement. This mixture, containing 1 sack of cement, 1 cubic foot of sand, and approximately 1½ cubic feet of coarse aggregate, is typical of topping which will withstand severe wear.

hardens, is used when the colored concrete can be placed and finished immediately as in driveways, tennis courts, walks, and pavements.

In the two-course method, the concrete for the base is mixed and placed as in ordinary work. The colored concrete is mixed and placed almost immediately so that it bonds with the base in a solid slab. On large jobs it is often desirable to have two mixers working, one being used for the colored concrete.

Concrete topping (Fig. 10) should not be applied until the base course (Fig. 11) has stiffened somewhat and all excess water has evaporated or has been removed with a broom, belt, float, or by other convenient means. Brooming, for example, re-

moves water, scum, and laitance, and produces a rough surface providing a good bond for the colored topping.

Delayed Two-Course Method

This method is best suited to floor work and similar construction where it is not desirable to place the topping until other construction work has been completed. When this method is to be used, it is best to leave the surface of the base course fairly rough to secure a good bond with the topping. Prior to placing the topping, the surface is thoroughly cleaned and dampened. A thin coat of cement grout is broomed onto the surface a short distance ahead of the topping as the latter is placed.

One-Course Method

Where the full thickness of concrete is placed, as in the one-course method, placing is much the same as in ordinary work. However, it is seldom economical, except for thin slabs or when only tints rather than deep colors are desired, to place the full thickness with colored concrete.

Placing Colored Topping

In either the two-course or delayed two-course method, placing of the topping is essentially the same. The minimum thickness of this topping usually is ½ inch for light wear or moderate exposure; 1 inch for heavy wear or severe exposure. As soon as the topping is placed it is leveled off with a strikeboard and given a wood-float finish.

Dust-on Color

For some floors subject only to light foot traffic, a dusted-on color mixture has been used. A 1-inch wearing course as recommended for heavy-duty floors is placed, and after screening to the proper level a dusted-on mixture is applied immediately. This mixture is made in the proportions of about 1 part portland cement, 1 to 1½ parts of sand, and the required amount of pigment. The sand should be well-graded with at least 80 per cent passing a No. 8 sieve, and not more than 3 per cent passing a No. 30 sieve. The mixture should be applied uniformly at the rate of not less than 125 pounds per 100 square feet of floor area.

After spreading, the dry material should be floated and worked into the slab. The first floating should be discontinued as soon as the surface becomes wet. Floating should be resumed when surface moisture has disappeared. After testing with a straightedge to eliminate high and low spots, the surface should be troweled to a smooth finish free from defects or blemishes. The concrete should then be cured as recommended for other floor finishes.

Finishing Colored Topping

Where a smoother finish than that imparted by the wood float is desired, the surface is left undisturbed for 30 to 45 minutes depending upon the temperature and weather conditions. When all the surface water has disappeared and there is no visible sheen, the concrete is finished lightly with a steel trowel (Fig. 12). It is important to trowel only in one direction to get uniform color.

Fig. 11. Placing base course for two-course color work in building a concrete tennis court. Note that a section of topping is already in place and finished.

Fig. 12. Troweling colored topping on a two-course concrete job where the topping is placed before the base course hardens. Note that the concrete is stiff enough to hold a man's weight.

Too much emphasis cannot be placed on the necessity for extreme care in the use of the steel trowel. An expert can, with a minimum amount of steel troweling, develop a beautiful, smooth surface which will be free from dusting or checking and which will have good wearing quality. A good point to keep in mind is that the fewer strokes required to produce a smooth surface, the better will be the job.

Curing

The proper curing of colored concrete is important to the success of the job for it develops strength, watertightness, and resistance to wear. Recommended methods of curing are discussed on Pg. 13.

Dusting

Dusting or wearing of concrete surfaces usually indicates a defective finish due, in most cases, to improper finishing and curing. If fresh concrete is troweled too much, fine material is drawn to the top resulting in a surface which lacks durability. It is never good practice to sprinkle dry cement or a mixture of cement and fine aggregate on concrete to take up surface water. Such fine materials form a layer on the surface that is likely to dust or hair check when the concrete hardens.

If a concrete surface is not allowed to cure properly it does not become hard and lacks durability. Proper curing and finishing are the best preventive measures for defective finishes and subsequent dusting.

Efflorescence

Efflorescence, sometimes called blooming, is a deposit on the surface and in the pores of masonry building materials such as brick, clay, tile, limestone, marble, terra cotta, and concrete. It is usually due to the passage of water out of the material carrying soluble substances dissolved from some constituent of the material. When this water reaches the surface and evaporates, the substances are deposited.

This deposit usually being whitish in color is particularly noticeable and objectionable on colored concrete surfaces. Obviously if concrete is made watertight, the likelihood of efflorescence is reduced to a minimum. Proper proportioning of the mixture, the use of not more than 5 gallons of water per sack of cement, thorough mixing and proper placing, finishing, and curing will produce watertight colored concrete.

Removing Efflorescence

Where efflorescence occurs, it may be dissolved by a dilute solution of muriatic acid (1 part of concentrated acid to 10 parts of water). In using this treatment the surface of the concrete is wetted before applying the acid and is thoroughly washed after the acid treatment.

The length of time required for the acid solution to dissolve efflorescence will depend upon the amount of the latter. In most cases, the acid can be washed off within three or four minutes. It is best not to leave the acid solution on longer than four minutes, for it may etch the colored concrete. If some deposit still remains after the first application, a second can be made. Acid solution should be brushed on smoothly, using the least amount possible.

Efflorescence also can be removed with a solution of equal parts of paraffin oil and benzine rubbed vigorously into the surface when the concrete is dry. This treatment also improves the wearing qualities of the surface by filling the pores and bringing out the color more uniformly. It is frequently applied to concrete surfaces for these reasons only.

Cleaning Colored Concrete

Colored concrete surfaces may be cleaned and made more impervious by washing with liquid soap. When this treatment is used the soap should be applied and allowed to stand over night, being washed off thoroughly next morning.

The application of ordinary floor wax once a month after the concrete is dry and clean will produce deep colors, improve the wearing surface and make it easy to keep clean. After the first two or three waxings, unless the surface is to be subjected to unusually severe wear, waxing twice a year will be sufficient.

Mechanical Scoring

Interesting effects or patterns can be obtained on concrete floors by cutting grooves to form the pattern. A standard electric hand saw fitted with a carborundum wheel and mounted on a straight edge is equipment often used for this operation. The score marks should not be cut deep, about 1/32 of an inch is sufficient. This depth cuts through the surface finish to show a joint and does not form deep grooves to hold dirt or cause rough joints in the floor.

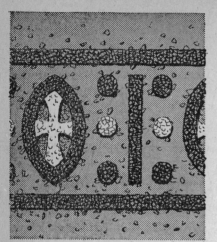

Fig. 13. A beautiful texture obtained through the use of selected aggregates exposed by scrubbing.

SPECIAL SURFACE FINISHES

Concrete may be handled to produce a great variety of surface finishes. Some finishes are partly arranged for when the materials are selected, others are imparted by the forms, and others are produced entirely after the concrete has hardened.

Concrete that will be subjected to treatments for producing special surface finishes must be made with well graded aggregates which are attractive when exposed or cut. Such concrete also must be fairly stiff when placed to prevent segregation—that is, to make certain that aggregates will be uniformly distributed.

Use of Selected Aggregates

Among the most attractive finishes are those which are pre-arranged when mixing the materials. Aggregates are selected for their color as well as for their ability to take polish. Among the aggregates commonly used are white sand, marble chips, granite screenings, crushed felspar, mica-spar, crushed slag, garnet sand and similar colored rock materials.

The mixtures are prepared and placed in the usual way and surface finish secured by washing off the surface film of cement exposing the aggregates and revealing their color (Fig. 13).

When forms are removed within 24 hours the surface film of cement usually can be washed off by spraying with water under pressure, or by scrubbing with a stiff brush and water. When the concrete has become too hard to yield to this treatment, an acid wash consisting of one part muriatic acid to four or five parts of water is used. The wash is applied with a brush scrubbing lightly until the film of cement has been removed. The surface is thoroughly washed with clean water immediately afterwards to remove all traces of the acid to prevent further action.

A wide variety of colors and textures may be secured by exposing the aggregate. Different combinations of materials produce different effects. A mix of yellow and white marble chips or a mixture of gray granite screenings and black crushed slag with a little mica-spar are examples.

Finishes Imparted by Forms

Surface finishes imparted to the concrete by the forms may be smooth, rough, paneled, or fashioned in almost any manner desired (Fig. 14). If wooden forms (Fig. 15) are used, they are constructed of tongue-and-groove material, evenly matched and tightly fitted. It is best to construct them in sections of such dimensions and shapes as will make their removal easy without undue hammering and without prying against the face of the concrete. Small openings in the forms may be pointed flush with stiff clay or plaster of Paris in order to prevent leakage or the formation of fins.

Wherever possible, it is best to employ skilled carpenters to construct forms for exposed concrete.

Rubbed Finish

Decorative treatments which may be produced after the concrete has

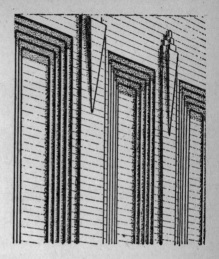

Fig. 15. An attractive surface finish developed through the use of uniform sizes of lumber in the forms. As soon as forms were removed, the concrete was dampened and then rubbed with carborundum stones.

Fig. 14. Practically any desired finish may be imparted to concrete by the forms. In this concrete the board marks and the grain of the wood are reproduced.

hardened include finishes developed by the use of rubbing methods, scrubbing (Fig. 16), sand blasting (Fig. 17), tooling, bush hammering (Fig. 18), sand floating, and cement washing.

In producing the "rubbed finish" the forms are removed as soon as possible. The surface is then wet thoroughly and scrubbed with No. 20 carborundum stones while the concrete is still "green." The lather that works up on the surface is removed by brushing and washing. Small voids in the surface are filled with a mortar composed of 1 part portland cement and 2 parts of the same kind of sand as that used in the facing concrete. This mortar is worked into the face with carborundum stones so that no appreciable thickness of coat-

Fig. 16. Exposing aggregates by scrubbing with a stiff wire brush and water. Where concrete is hardened somewhat it is often necessary to use a solution of muriatic acid and water.

ing remains. A coating of any appreciable thickness is to be avoided as it may peel off and crack.

Several weeks after the first rubbing, and when the concrete has attained a considerable degree of hardness, the surfaces again are rubbed down. This time No. 24 carborundum stones and water are used. Again a lather will be worked up which is removed with a clean wet brush. While this amount of rubbing produces an attractive surface, it usually does not remove form marks.

Scrubbed Finish

To produce a "scrubbed" or "brush" finish, the forms are removed while the concrete is still quite "green" and the surface is scrubbed with wire brushes, water being used freely. The scrubbing is continued until the surface film of mortar is removed and the aggregate is uniformly exposed. The surface is then rinsed with water. If parts of the

surface have become too hard to scrub in equal relief, diluted muriatic acid (1 part acid to 4 or 5 parts water) may be used. Remove all acid with clean water after scrubbing is done to prevent further action.

The best time to begin scrubbing is learned by experience. If begun too soon, unsightly voids may be made by scrubbing out pieces of aggregate. If the scrubbing is not started soon enough, the concrete will be so hard that the brush will not remove the surface mortar.

It is almost impossible to obtain sharp corners in scrubbed work and for this reason fillets of rounded moldings usually are placed in the forms so as to leave no sharp corners.

Sand-Blast Finish

Another method used to expose the aggregate is sand blasting the

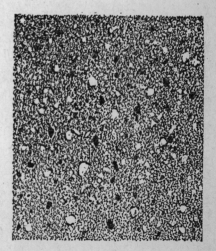

Fig. 17. Sand blasting produces a surface texture like this in which some of the aggregates are partially exposed.

surface with hard sand until the desired degree of relief is obtained. A concrete surface thus treated must have become fairly hard. The equipment necessary for sand blasting is large and, therefore, seldom is used on small jobs because of a comparatively high cost.

FORMS FOR CONCRETE

Any good, sound lumber free from knots and decay, is suitable for form work. The use of sheathing lumber dressed on one side and both edges is recommended because forms built of it are easy to remove. Where smooth, true surfaces are required, it is best to use lumber that is dressed on all four sides. Tight joints are obtained by using tongue-and-groove stock or shiplap. To prevent waste,

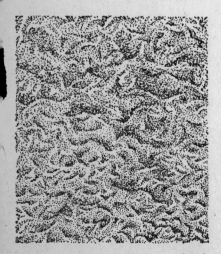

Fig. 18. A typical finish which is produced by bush hammering hardened concrete. Almost any type of finish may be imparted by bush hammering or tooling.

lumber is bought in the nearest commercial length to the height or length of the forms.

The sizes of lumber commonly used in form work are: 1-inch stock for floor, foundation and wall forms, columns and beam sides; 2-inch stock for beam bottoms and heavy concrete construction; 2 by 4-inch stock for form studs, column yokes and framing for panels; 2 by 6, or 2 by 8-inch stock for stringers and joists; 3 by 4, or 4 by 4-inch stock for posts, struts, shores, uprights, and sometimes for stringers; 1 or 2-inch stock for cleats; and 1 by 6-inch stock for cross ties and similar bracing.

Form Construction

Forms may be built in sections or panels so constructed that they can be easily removed and used again, or so that the lumber in them can be knocked down without injury and used in other work (Fig. 19). Contractors often construct forms with special double-headed nails, or with screws instead of common wire nails. It is well to design forms so they can be taken down with the least amount of hammering, thus preventing possible injury to the concrete before it has thoroughly hardened.

Forms often can be assembled in part by clamps and wedges, and only a few nails partly driven will be needed. Metal pans, adjustable shores and wire ties are other accessories commonly used. Where wire ties are used, they are tightened by twisting. Spacers are removed as concreting progresses.

Fig. 19. Well-built forms are essential to good concrete work. Such forms are easily removed.

To prevent adhesion of the concrete and to make form removal easy, it is customary to oil the faces which come in contact with the concrete. Crude oil, oil drained from crank cases, or soft soap is generally used and is applied with swab or brush. Whitewash is sometimes used instead of oil or soap. Forms are cleaned and again oiled each time before reusing.

Oil, whitewash, and similar materials should not be applied to surfaces of forms coming in contact with concrete to be painted or stuccoed.

Conduits, Pipes, and Openings

Where construction requires the installation of conduits, pipes, and other service leads, these are preferably put in position before concrete is placed.

All conduits and pipes are so situated as not to reduce the strength of the concrete construction. For ex-

ample, where concrete floors are to be surfaced with wood flooring, pipes or conduits are usually placed between the sleepers. When other types of floor finishes are used, conduits or pipes are placed in the top slab of concrete joist or tile and joist floors, and in the bottom of solid slab floors, usually just above the reinforcing steel. In concrete joist floors, pipes or conduits may be placed in the spaces between the joists.

Conduits or pipes should never be placed in joists or other load-carrying members as such construction reduces their strength. For the same reason, building codes and specifications generally require that outlet boxes for electrical fixtures or other openings be kept out of concrete joists and other structural members. Wood generally is used for forming square or rectangular openings; sheet metal for curved openings.

Removal of Forms

In summer weather, wall forms generally can be stripped after one or two days, and in cooler weather in from four to seven days. Concrete floors, roofs, and other similar construction are not stripped in less than seven days in summer, and fourteen days in colder weather. A good rule to follow is that forms must never be removed until it is certain that the concrete has hardened sufficiently to be self-sustaining.

Special Forms

In ornamental concrete work, where the making of complex shapes is necessary, glue, plaster, and other special molds are employed. Considerable skill is required in their manufacture and use. Usually contractors prefer to purchase ornamental molds from cast stone manufacturers, ornamental plastering contractors, or companies specializing in molds for making ornamental concrete.

REINFORCED CONCRETE

Reinforcement is the term used to describe the steel bars, or the small or large mesh metal reinforcement placed in concrete to increase its tensile strength. Concrete is a material which is very strong in compression—that is, very strong in bearing loads that are placed directly upon it, but it requires steel bars or other metal reinforcement in some structures to increase its power to resist stresses or forces that tend to bend or pull it apart. In a concrete lintel over a door or a window opening or in a beam, for example, reinforcement is placed near the lower side, as that is the side which tends to pull apart when the lintel or beam is loaded.

On most work, sizes, location, and spacing of reinforcement usually are determined in advance by experienced engineers, blueprints showing details of construction being furnished. Where it is necessary for the contractor to determine the sizes and spacing of reinforcement, it is recommended that he consult an engineer experienced in reinforced concrete design.

WATERTIGHT CONCRETE

Watertight construction will result when the concrete itself is made watertight and when workmanship is such that all seams and other construction joints will resist the passage of water. Leakage through concrete walls, for example, often is due to openings in seams rather than to the lack of watertightness in the concrete itself. How to make watertight seams is discussed on Page 11.

One of the main reasons for making concrete watertight is that moisture entering concrete may result in structural defects. For example, the water may freeze and break the bond between the cement paste and aggregates, thus lowering the quality of the concrete.

Making Watertight Concrete

The essential requirement for watertight concrete is the use of durable aggregates which are completely coated with a cement paste that resists the passage of water. Leakage through concrete, if any, usually is through the paste, and it can be prevented by having a sufficient quantity of watertight paste to coat all particles of aggregate and to fill all spaces between them. The recommended amount of mixing water to produce a watertight paste, is not more than 6 gallons for each sack of cement including whatever moisture may be contained in the aggregates. *See the* PROPORTIONING TABLE *on Page 4.*

Mixing and Placing

To insure that concrete will be watertight, it is necessary to have a plastic, workable mixture that can be thoroughly spaded to fill the forms without segregation of the materials. Thorough mixing, therefore, is required. This produces uniform batches, completely coats the aggregates with cement paste and makes the concrete more plastic, thus helping to make placing easier.

It is best practice to use methods of handling that will permit the concrete to be transported and placed without segregation of the materials and to continue placing without stopping if possible. Where interruptions cannot be avoided it is necessary to obtain good bond with the hardened concrete.

Favorable curing conditions are essential in making watertight con-

Fig. 20. Heating materials is an essential operation when doing concrete work in cold weather.

crete. Recommended practice is to moist cure the concrete from 5 to 7 days, preferably for two weeks or longer when it is practical to do so. As pointed out in the discussion on *Curing* on Page 13, keeping concrete moist and at proper temperatures, beginning soon after it is placed, is the most effective means of making concrete that is dense and watertight.

HIGH EARLY STRENGTH CONCRETE

Contractors often are required to produce concrete having comparatively high strength a few days after it is placed. This can be accomplished by using a larger quantity of normal portland cement or by using high early strength portland cement.

Using Normal Portland Cement

Concrete having high early strength can be made with normal portland cement by reducing the total quantity of water mixed with each sack of cement. For example, concrete made with 4½ gallons per sack is about twice as strong at 3 days as concrete made with 7 gallons per sack. The lower water cement ratio, however, will require additional cement to produce the same consistency.

The rate of hardening can be increased by dissolving flake calcium chloride in the mixing water. The quantity used should not exceed 2 pounds for each sack of cement; the proper amount to use will depend upon the temperature prevailing at the time of concreting. For temperatures below 80 degrees F., use 2 pounds per sack of cement. For temperatures between 80 and 90 degrees F., use 1½ pounds per sack of cement, and for temperatures above 90 degrees F., 1 pound per sack of cement.

Using High Early Strength Portland Cement

In general, the high early strength cements now commonly available are made from the same kinds of materials and in the same manner as normal portland cements. They harden in the same way but more rapidly. For the same quantity of water per sack of cement and the same curing conditions, concrete made with high early strength portland cement will be about as strong at 1 day as concrete made with normal portland cement will be at 3 days. At 7 days the strength will be about equal to the 28-day strength of concrete made with normal portland cement.

Regardless of cement used, concrete, to attain high early strength, should be kept at a temperature of 70 degrees or above, beginning soon after it is placed. Concrete cured at temperatures below 70 degrees hardens more slowly and is not likely to have high strength at an early age.

COLD WEATHER CONSTRUCTION

Concrete can be made during cold weather just as well as at any other time—in fact, contractors do millions of dollars' worth of concrete construction every winter. Winter work has certain advantages. Labor of all kinds, skilled and unskilled, generally is plentiful and overhead expenses are reduced by keeping equipment in continuous use.

Heat hastens the hardening of concrete; cold retards it. When concrete is placed in the forms it is best that it have a temperature of not less than 60 degrees nor more than 80 degrees F. In cold weather the concrete must be maintained at a temperature of 50 degrees or higher for at least five days after placing.

In early winter, when freezing temperatures occur only at night, it is necessary merely to protect concrete from freezing after it is placed. As the weather grows colder and freezing temperatures prevail, the mixing water and aggregates are heated and the work protected as well.

Heating Water

Water is commonly heated in a large kettle, wash boiler, or similar container supported over a fire. Water also can be heated by discharging live steam into it. Regardless of the method employed in heating (Fig. 20), it is best to take care that the temperature of the water is never greater than 175 degrees F. when it comes in contact with the cement in the mixture; otherwise a flash set may take place. However, boiling water may be added to the aggregates before cement is included. The aggregates cool the water to a point where danger of a flash set is eliminated.

Heating Aggregates

Several methods of heating sand and other aggregates are commonly used. The materials may be banked over a metal barrel laid on its side, a section of smokestack, or some other improvised heater, and a fire kindled inside. A satisfactory heater, for small jobs can be made by building a fire-box of concrete masonry units with a sheet-iron cover on which the aggregates are piled.

Sand and coarse aggregate are heated separately to prevent them from becoming mixed. They are turned frequently so that frost and ice are thawed out.

Mixing and Placing Concrete

While the concrete is made as stiff as possible, obtain a mix that will place and finish well. Concrete is placed immediately after mixing to prevent loss of heat. Frost, snow, and ice, when present, are removed from the forms before the concrete is placed.

If the ground on which concrete is to be placed is frozen, it should be thawed out before placing the concrete. In cold weather work it is customary and good practice to have excavating done before the ground is frozen. Then the excavated areas are covered with straw or other suitable coverings to protect the earth from freezing.

CHAPTER 2

BRICKLAYING

Man has been making bricks out of clay for an estimated 12,000 years. Clay is ground fine, pressed into the shape of a brick, and fired or dried in a kiln at a temperature of approximately 2,000° F. for two or three days or longer.

Bricks were first made in America a few years following the settlement of the English colonists in the seventeenth century. Originally manufactured by hand, bricks are now nearly all made by automatic machines.

Kinds of Bricks

There are many kinds of brick but the four most common types are: common brick, face brick, fire brick, and vitrified brick.

Common brick is the usual red type which can be purchased at the lumber yard in practically any town or city. Its size is always 8 inches long, 3¾ inches wide, and 2½ inches thick.

Face brick is generally the same size as common brick but comes in other sizes as well. It is made more carefully and generally of better materials, comes in a variety of colors and finishes, and is often made to order. Face brick is sometimes called enameled or glazed brick.

Fire brick is especially made for use in fireplaces, ovens and chimneys, where the flame or high temperature

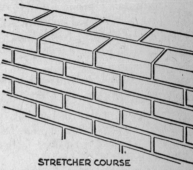

STRETCHER COURSE

Fig. 1. The "stretcher" course wherein bricks are laid flat, and end to end.

touch the brickwork. It is made of a particular kind of clay that resists intense heat without crumbling. Dried differently than other brick, it is repressed after partially dry and then fired again. Fire brick is generally 9 inches long, 4½ inches wide, and 2½ inches thick.

Courses

Each row of bricks is called a "course." There are two main types: 1, the "stretcher" course wherein bricks are laid flat and end to end (Fig. 1), and 2, the "header" course wherein bricks are laid flat and side by side, (Fig. 2).

Bricks laid in a header course naturally form a wall 8 inches thick as bricks are 8 inches long. The 8-inch width is generally considered as the minimum thickness for any indepen-

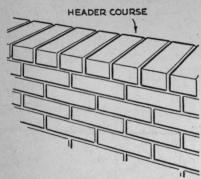

HEADER COURSE

Fig. 2. The "header" course wherein bricks are laid flat, and side by side.

dent brick wall. Two stretcher courses laid side by side, with mortar between them, form a wall 8 inches thick.

In both stretcher and header courses bricks are laid on their 3¾ by 8-inch surfaces. When laid on their sides, the 2¼ by 8-inch surfaces, they are said to be laid "on face," or in a "rowlock course."

Bond

A brick wall is made by laying several courses, one above another, and the arrangement of the courses is called the bond. Actually, it is the pattern of the wall.

The commonest arrangement, called "common bond," is shown in Fig. 3. In it you will notice that there are 5 stretcher courses topped by a header course. If the wall is built higher, five more stretcher courses will be followed by another header course. This process continues to the top of the wall. As the width of the bricks on the stretcher course is only 3¾ inches, a second stretcher course has to be laid beside the first, with

mortar between, to make the total width 8 inches. The header course will then tie in these two courses and prevent the wall from coming apart in the middle.

Another type of bond, shown in Fig. 4, is called "English bond." In this bond courses of headers and stretchers alternate. A header course is laid first and then two stretcher courses side by side on top of it. Then comes another header course and so on. In laying two stretcher courses alongside of each other, be sure to stagger the vertical joints. This rule applies to all vertical joints. The joints must be staggered so that one will not come on top of another.

A third type of bond is "Flemish bond" shown in Fig. 5, in which each course is a combination of headers and stretchers. With each successive course the headers center on the stretchers in the course below.

Bricklaying Tools

Professional bricklayers use a wide variety of tools to speed up the work

COMMON BOND

Fig. 3. In Common Bond, 5 stretcher courses are topped by a header course.

of laying bricks. As far as the home handyman is concerned he can readily get along with a trowel, a spirit level, heavy hammer, raker, and a cold chisel, (Fig. 6). The level should be about 2 feet long, and of the type that can be used to check both vertical and horizontal lines. Do not try to judge whether the wall is plumb merely by looking at it. Use the level often to make certain. A good way to keep each course horizontal is to stretch a cotton line or fishline along the face of the wall as a guide.

Another way to help insure that your brick wall is straight is to make and use a straight edge. Take a seasoned piece of lumber 10 to 12 feet long, 6 inches wide, and 1 to 2 inches thick. Finish one edge so it is perfectly straight and true. The ends of the other edge can be beveled down from the 6 inch width to about 1 inch to decrease the weight and make it easier to handle. Use this straight edge to check that the sides of your wall are straight and that the tops of each course of brick are horizontal.

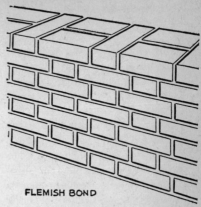

FLEMISH BOND

Fig. 5. In Flemish Bond, each course is a combination of headers and stretchers.

Joints

There are numerous ways to finish the outside of the mortar joints between bricks so that they will look attractive, (Fig. 7). The commonest method is the *flush joint,* but this does not wear too well on exterior brick surfaces as water drains down, dampens the mortar and eventually wears some of it away. The *concave joint* is one that is easily made with a raker having a bevelled edge. The mortar should be permitted to set for a few minutes before this joint is made. The *struck joint* and the *weathered joint* are made by using the point of the trowel. The *raked joint* is probably the most difficult to make, and amateur bricklayers would do well to avoid it.

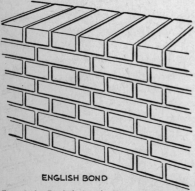

ENGLISH BOND

Fig. 4. In English Bond, courses of headers and stretchers are alternated throughout.

MORTAR

The key to strong brickwork is the mortar. A well constructed brick wall will keep out water, but if poorly constructed, in due time the wind will drive rain into the wall that will drain out on the other side. The chief ingredients of mortar are portland cement, sand, clean water, and sometimes hydrated lime. If lime is used, it replaces that much cement. The proportion most generally advocated is one part portland cement to three parts sand, and enough water to make the mixture pliable. That proportion forms the strongest mortar and should be used wherever brick masonry is exposed to weather, fire, water, vibration, or load. However, such mortar sets quickly and is therefore more difficult to use.

Ten per cent lime is the name of another mortar formula. In this, the three parts of sand are added to one part of portland cement and hydrated lime, the one part consisting of 90 per cent cement and 10 per cent lime. This mixture is easier to use than the one above.

The cheapest type of mortar is known as 1 : 1 : 6; meaning one part of portland cement, one part of hydrated lime, and six parts of sand, plus water. This type is satisfactory for backing-up masonry such as the inside of the wall of a house, and is easy to use.

Using the 1 : 1 : 6 mortar mix, the following are the amounts of each ingredient needed to produce enough mortar to build 100 square feet of brick wall:

	8″ wall Thickness of joint			12″ wall Thickness of joint			12¼″ wall Thickness of joint		
	⅜″	½″	⅝″	⅜″	½″	⅝″	⅜″	½″	⅝″
Cement, bags	2.55	3.07	3.51	3.84	4.58	5.26	4.17	4.93	5.60
Lime, lbs.	102	123	141	154	184	210	167	197	224
Sand, cu. ft.	0.57	0.68	0.78	0.86	1.02	1.17	0.93	1.10	1.25

A bag of cement weighs 94 pounds. Lime comes in bags weighing 50 pounds. A cu. ft. of dry sand weighs from 90 to 120 pounds.

By getting current prices of bricks, cement, lime, and sand from your neighborhood dealer, you can figure out the approximate cost of materials for brickwork planned. However, the above tables give no allowance for waste and you must allow a little for that.

Mixing Mortar

It will prove helpful to build a mixing box as near as practicable to the site of your bricklaying operations

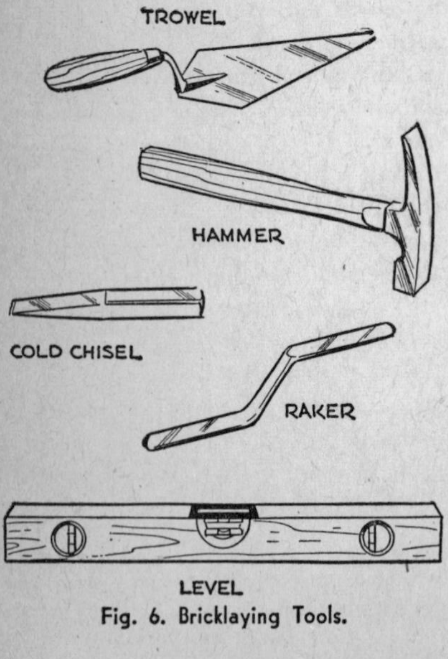

TROWEL

HAMMER

COLD CHISEL

RAKER

LEVEL

Fig. 6. Bricklaying Tools.

as the less distance you have to carry mortar the better. Use planks 1 or 2 inches thick to form a box about 8 feet long, 4 feet wide, and with sides 8 or 10 inches high. The end pieces should slant at an angle of about 45 degrees. Nail the floor of box to cross pieces under it. Then nail the sides to diagonal end pieces, and finally toenail the sides to the floor of the box.

Similarly, a large metal wheelbarrow can be used as a mixing box. Use a pail or small box for measuring your ingredients. Put the sand in first, three pails full. Then, if you are using the 3 and 1 mix, add a pail full of cement.

If you are using the 1 : 1 : 6 mix, add ½ pail of cement to the 3 of sand, mix it in well with a shovel or hoe, and finally add ½ pail of hydrated lime mixing it in well.

Add water slowly and mix it in well with hoe or shovel. When the mixture is stiff, add a little more water and stir some more. When the mortar becomes smooth and plastic and falls from a shovel or hoe as a soft mass, it is ready to use. It should not be watery. If you get too much water in it by mistake, add more sand and cement within the proportions you are following.

Planning Brickwork

Before any mortar is mixed and spread you should lay out the whole first course of brick the full length of the job to see if you come out with an even number of bricks. Allow about ½ inch between bricks. Then increase or decrease the space be-tween each brick to make the bricks come out even. That is usually possible on distances of 8 feet or more. On shorter walls you may have to use a partial brick. Cutting bricks can be done with the cold chisel and hammer.

The following table gives the probable number of bricks needed to build 100 square feet of wall, that is, a wall 10 feet long and 10 feet high:

Thickness of joint	8 inch wall	12 inch wall	16 inch wall
⅜ inch	1310	1965	2620
½ inch	1232	1848	2465
⅝ inch	1161	1742	2322

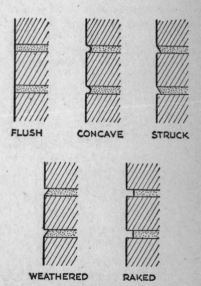

FLUSH   CONCAVE   STRUCK

WEATHERED   RAKED

Fig. 7. There are numerous ways to finish the outside of mortar joints between bricks so that they will look attractive. Five such joints are illustrated above.

LAYING BRICK

Lay the end bricks first. Spread mortar with your trowel on the foundation to form what is called the bed joint and place the brick on it, (Fig. 8). For details on how to construct a foundation see the material on *Foundations* in *Chapter 3*. Press the brick down so it is ½ inch from the founda-

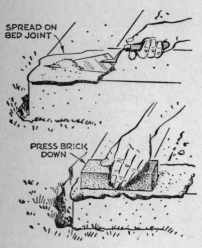

SPREAD ON BED JOINT

PRESS BRICK DOWN

Fig. 8. Spread mortar with your trowel on the foundation to form what is called the bed joint. Place the brick on it and press down so that the brick rests ½ inch from the foundation.

tion. Scrape up excess mortar. Soak or immerse bricks in a pail of water before laying them. If this is not done the dry brick will absorb so much water from the mortar that it will dry out too soon and not bond well. Then the mortar will crumble away after it dries and you will have cracks in your wall.

After both end bricks of a course are laid, stretch a taut line from one end to the other to aid you in setting the rest of the bricks in an exact straight line. Your eye is not exact enough, and it is essential to have the foundation course exactly straight.

Expert bricklayers pick up enough mortar on a trowel to form a bed joint for four or five bricks, but the novice will do well to place just enough mortar for one brick at a time. Place some mortar against the head of the brick already laid and also on the head of the next brick to be laid so that the head joint (between the ends of two bricks) will be solidly filled. Surplus mortar squeezed out of joints should be picked up with the trowel and placed on the bed for the next brick.

Try to avoid picking up a brick after it has been laid in position, for if a brick is moved once the mortar has begun to set, the bond will not be perfect, and slight cracks may result that will allow water to get into the wall.

Continue placing plenty of mortar at the head of each brick laid. Any excess will be squeezed up and be used in the bed joint for the next course.

Closure Brick

When you come to the last brick (called the "closure" brick) to be laid in a course, be sure to place mortar on the ends of both bricks already in place, and on both ends of the closure brick, (Fig. 9).

If you come to the end of a course of brick and find you have misjudged and left too much or too little space for the last brick, do not go back and try to tap several bricks closer or farther apart. Remove all the bricks you need to shift and all the mortar holding them, and relay them with fresh mortar.

When removing excess mortar squeezed out when a brick is laid, lift the trowel upwards rather than sideways. Also, lift up slightly in the direction of bricks already laid rather than away from laid bricks. Failure to do this may result in small cracks in either the head or bed joints.

Speed and accuracy are important in laying brick. You must get bricks in place before mortar sets and you you must lay them straight and fill the joints completely. After each course is laid, raise your guide line another brick's thickness. Check with your straight edge frequently to make sure bricks are laid level.

After every three or four rows, before the mortar hardens, tool the joints with the raker. This presses the mortar tight against the brick on each side, and gives a concave finish.

Wall Variations

Of course if you are building a wall 4 inches wide, the width of one brick, and it goes in a straight line, each successive course will start with a half brick so that the head joints will be staggered. There might be cases where a low 4-inch thick wall would suffice, but in most cases a brick wall needs to be thicker than that.

An 8-inch wall is two bricks wide in stretcher courses. In common

bond every sixth course should be a header course. In English bond every other course is a header. The combination of header and stretcher courses gives a much more solid wall, more than twice as strong as 4-inch walls.

A 12-inch wall can be a combination of stretcher and header courses, with three rows of stretchers in some

CLOSURE BRICK

Fig. 9. When you come to the final brick (called the "closure" brick) to be laid in a course, be certain to place mortar on the ends of both bricks already in place, and on both ends of the closure brick.

courses. Such a wall is more than three times as solid as a 4-inch wall. If a number of bricks become broken, a 12-inch wall is ideal for using them. When laying three rows of stretcher courses, lay the two outside rows with full brick and mortar, and fill the center with mortar and broken pieces of brick, (Fig. 10).

An ordinary wall such as we have been considering should be topped with a ½-inch layer of concrete to help prevent water from settling in the joints and working down.

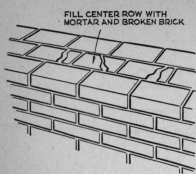

FILL CENTER ROW WITH
MORTAR AND BROKEN BRICK

Fig. 10. When laying three rows of stretcher courses, lay the two outside rows with full brick and mortar, and fill the center with mortar and broken pieces of brick.

Brick is produced in a variety of colors, some of which may harmonize in certain locations better than others. Also in recent years brick has been painted with cement or oil paint. However, painting brick walls does not usually add to the durability or weather resistance of the structure.

Corners

Most brickwork turns corners, and corners provide the means for staggering joints without using half bricks. There is nothing very complicated about a simple corner in common bond. Some of the more complicated patterns have fancy corners, but the novice will be wise not to attempt them.

CHAPTER 3

MASONRY PROJECTS

Herein is presented a series of masonry projects which the home handyman can readily accomplish with a basic understanding of the facts about concrete obtained from Chapter 1. Some of the more complicated projects, such as foundations and garages, are perhaps too ambitious for the amateur to undertake at first. However, with time, and following some successful experiments with the simpler ones, the more difficult projects can similarly be mastered.

BASEBALL HOME PLATE

If the playground nearby has a baseball diamond you can cast a concrete home plate either on the spot or at home. Fig. 1 gives the dimensions for the form. Note that these are inside dimensions of the form, to provide outside dimensions for the plate.

Use 1-inch thick lumber for the form. About 70 inches of it will be required for the sides. Other pieces of wood will be required to hold the form in place. Make the plate at least 3 inches thick. Use 1x4 inch lumber if desired.

For a 3-inch thick plate about 16 pounds of cement (or 1/6 sack) will be required, plus 4¼ quarts of water, 1/3 cu. ft. of sand, and 2/5 cu. ft. of gravel.

If you make the plate at home, place the form on oiled paper set on a flat surface. Let the concrete cure for about a week. Dig a hole at the ball field so that the top of the concrete home plate will be flush with the ground, and ball players will not be injured when sliding home.

BENCH

Concrete lawn or garden benches are often useful, require no maintenance, and add considerably to the

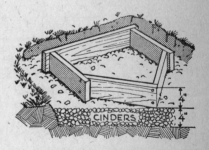

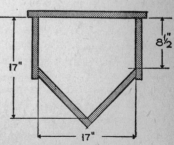

Fig. 1. Baseball home plate.

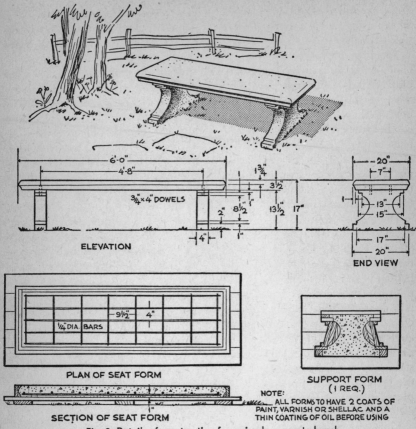

ELEVATION

END VIEW

PLAN OF SEAT FORM

SECTION OF SEAT FORM

SUPPORT FORM
(I REQ.)

NOTE:
ALL FORMS TO HAVE 2 COATS OF
PAINT, VARNISH OR SHELLAC AND A
THIN COATING OF OIL BEFORE USING

Fig. 2. Details of construction for a simple concrete bench.

appearance of a yard. Plans showing construction details for a simple but attractive bench are given in Fig. 2.

The seat mold or form is made of 1-inch boards which have been planed and sanded to insure that all inner surfaces of the form will be smooth and level. The inner sides of the seat form are lined with molding as shown, so that all edges will have a neat appearance. To prevent warping of the surfaces when damp concrete is placed in them both forms

should be coated with two coats of varnish or shellac. And just before the concrete is poured they should be given a coat of light lubricating oil.

Two ¾-inch holes are drilled in the bottom board form 4 feet 8 inches apart as indicated, and wooden plugs which stick up 2 inches are tightly inserted. These will provide holes for dowels which will key the seat to the supports.

Five steel rods ¼-inch round are placed 4 inches apart lengthwise as shown in the diagram to reinforce the seat. Eight more are placed crosswise 9½ inches apart.

The form for the supports is also built of 1-inch boards. The curved portions are made of galvanized sheet metal properly bent and braced. Dowel holes are also drilled in the support form and wooden plugs inserted, sticking out 2 inches. It will probably be easier to make just one form for the support and use it twice than to make two support forms and fill each one.

The proper concrete mixture for this type of work is shown in the table on Page 4. Place a layer of concrete 1 inch deep over the entire bottom of the seat form. Then place the reinforcing rods in position and add the remaining 2½ inches of concrete, tamping it into the form thoroughly. The reinforcing rods should never be less than 1 inch from the surface of the concrete. The surface can be leveled with a straightedge or planed board and then lightly troweled to give it a smooth surface.

Concrete for the supports is poured in the same manner. No reinforcement rods are needed. Run your trowel through the concrete to help remove air bubles and produce dense concrete with a smooth surface.

After the forms have been filled they should remain undisturbed for at least 24 hours and during colder weather, for 48 hours. Be careful not to injure the green concrete when removing the forms. Once removed, the supports and seat should be covered with straw and kept moist for at least 10 days.

The bench should not be set up for at least 4 and preferably 6 weeks. Hardwood plugs ¾-inch thick and 4 inches long should be used for dowels to attach the seat to the supports.

Footings

A good solid footing is essential for the proper placement of a concrete lawn bench. Footings should cover about double the area of each support, and a depth of 6 inches is usually sufficient.

To prepare footings, dig holes of the required size and depth and fill them with the same mix as used for the bench. Tamp well, level off and

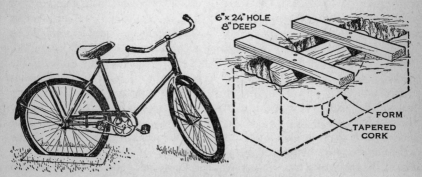

Fig. 3. Concrete bicycle stand.

allow the concrete to harden for 24 hours before placing the bench upon them.

BICYCLE STAND

A handy stand keeping bicycles erect but out of the way is easily built. An arc representing a portion of a circle of the same circumference as the wheel of the bicycle is inscribed upon a board just slightly thicker than the wheel. After sawing the board along the line, a cork or dowel that has been tapered is nailed to the arc at its lowest point. Dig a small rectangular hole about the size shown in Fig. 3 and insert the mold. Pour concrete around it and allow to set. Take care that the concrete does not get below the level of the plug as the hole so formed will serve as a drain.

BRIDGE

A bridge for crossing small streams can save upkeep labor if made of concrete. Of course it will be initially expensive, and how it would compare with the cost and upkeep of a similar bridge of wood or steel or both cannot be predicted. Herein are details on how to build a concrete bridge.

Fig. 4 shows how to build a bridge that will accommodate a 6-ton load. The table following indicates the reinforcement and slab thickness for four different spans. Bridges for heavier loads and greater spans, and for crossing streams that are subject to wash-outs require special considera-

tion. Dry weather and periods of low water are naturally the best times for such construction work.

Reinforcement and Slab Thickness
for Small Concrete Bridges

Clear span	Slab thickness	Reinforcement Diameter	K-rods Spacing
Feet	Inches	Inch	Inches
6	6½	⅝	8
9	6½	⅝	7
12	7	¾	8
15	8	¾	7

Note: Transverse reinforcing rods are ⅜-inch round rods placed 8 inches on centers.

To prevent undermining, the abutments must extend at least 2 feet below the bed of the stream. For greater security against erosion, rock or broken concrete, if available, could be laid as riprap, on the embankments next to the abutments. Forms for the abutments can be built much the same way as those for a basement or cellar wall. Naturally you pour the abutments first, leaving dowels sticking up.

The top or deck slab must be carefully supported. A platform of planks will be needed and these should be supported by 2″ by 6″ joists set 2 feet apart. The joists should be supported by 4″ by 4″ girders spaced about 4 feet on centers. Shoring is needed to hold up the girders and it should be wedged and braced securely.

The width of the bridge can be whatever distance you decide. The width between wheels of most cars is about 60 inches, thus 72 inches from inside of curb to inside of curb will normally be enough except for specially wide trucks or other vehicles. Note that four types of reinforcement rods should be used. The table gives sizes of proper reinforce-

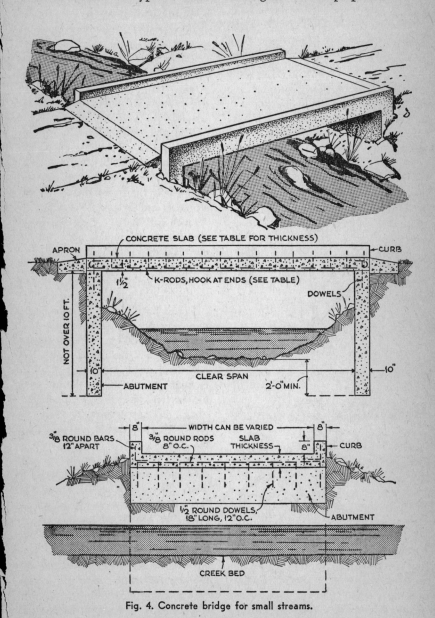

CONCRETE SLAB (SEE TABLE FOR THICKNESS)

APRON

CURB

1½"

K-RODS, HOOK AT ENDS (SEE TABLE)

DOWELS

NOT OVER 10 FT.

10"

10"

ABUTMENT

CLEAR SPAN

2'-0" MIN.

⅜" ROUND BARS 12" APART

8"

WIDTH CAN BE VARIED

8"

⅜" ROUND RODS 8" O.C.

SLAB THICKNESS

8"

CURB

½" ROUND DOWELS, 18" LONG, 12" O.C.

ABUTMENT

CREEK BED

Fig. 4. Concrete bridge for small streams.

ment K-rods and transverse rods for the slab. Fig. 4 shows how ½-inch round dowels anchor the slab to the abutments, and how ⅜-inch right angle bars reinforce the curbs.

The abutments can be a 1:3:5 mix and the concrete slab should be a 1:2½:3½ mix.

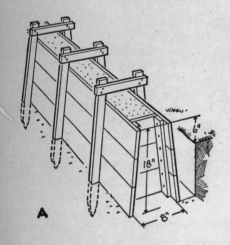

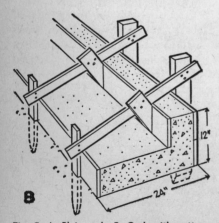

Fig. 5. A. Plain curb. B. Curb with gutter.

CURBS

Curbs are frequently used in connection with the various types of paving. They may be of either two-course or one-course construction, but the tendency is toward one-course work, that is, the same mixture throughout: 1:2½:3½ (cement, sand, gravel).

The plain curb is usually built so that it is 18 to 24 inches deep, 8 to 10 inches thick at the bottom, and 6 to 8 inches thick at the top. Fig. 5A shows how the forms should be constructed and braced. Note that an 18-inch curb has 6 inches of it above ground and 12 inches below. If the curb is deeper, only part of the added depth should be above ground. With a 24-inch deep curb, only 7 or 8 inches should be above ground.

Forms for alternate sections 5 or 6 feet long can be built and the concrete poured. When the concrete in these sections has set and has become self-sustaining, the forms can be removed, set up for the intervening sections, and the latter poured.

Fig. 5B shows how to construct forms for a combined curb and gutter. This should be built in sections no more than 10 feet in length, and expansion joints should be provided every 25 feet. Generally a gutter is formed at the intersection of a curb with the street paving, and care should be taken to pitch the gutter toward outlets or drains.

Plain curbs of reinforced concrete may be precast in sections 4 to 8 feet long. These are usually 4 to 8 inches thick and 18 to 24 inches high. The

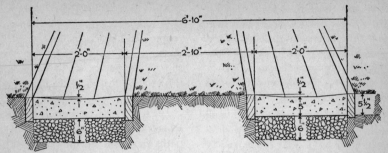

Fig. 6. Ribbon type driveway.

reinforcement may consist of longitudinally laid rods ¼ inch in diameter, spaced 6 inches apart. A piece of heavy woven-wire fencing 1 inch shorter in length and height than the curb section makes a satisfactory reinforcement. The wire should not be less than No. 10 gage.

DRIVEWAYS

A sturdy concrete driveway from the street to your garage will be convenient for you and your family, and will facilitate the delivery of fuel and other articles, and will improve the general appearance of your property. Driving over bare ground develops ruts, bumpy, uneven surfaces, and often mudholes that splash when you drive through them.

There are two types of concrete driveways that you can build. One is the ribbon type (Fig. 6), which consists of two concrete ribbons 2 feet wide with a space of 2 feet 10 inches between them. This is the less expensive type to build, but even with curbs on the outer edges of the ribbons there is always the chance of a driver running off the ribbons and messing up the adjacent ground. The slab type of concrete driveway shown in Fig. 7 is much better as there is less danger of driving off it.

Widths of Driveways

Since most cars are driven forward into a garage and backed out, driveways used for backing should be wider than those used for forward driving only.

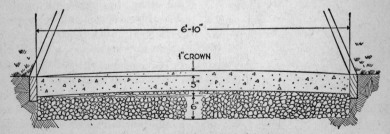

Fig. 7. A simple type of concrete slab driveway.

The following discussion of driveway widths presumes that the driveways will be used by backing vehicles. For short driveways that are to be used by vehicles moving forward only, the recommended widths might be reduced about 4 inches.

Passenger cars are fairly well standardized with regard to several of the dimensions that influence the design of driveways. The range of dimensions of most passenger cars on our highways is as follows: distance between front wheels, 55 to 61 inches; distance between rear wheels, 56 to 63 inches; turning radius (radius of the smallest circle that the outside front wheel will trace in turning), 18 to 25 feet; and overall width, 69 to 78 inches. The length of the wheel base, a very important dimension affecting the design of curved driveways, ranges from 112 to 154 inches.

Another dimension that must sometimes be considered is the distance from the front axle to the front extremity (bumper) of the car. As shown in Fig. 8, this overhang requires a clearance, d, beyond the outside front wheel when the car is on a curve. For most cars this overhang ranges between 26 and 33 inches. On a 30-foot radius curve, a car having a front overhang of 29 inches and a wheelbase of 112 inches will require an additional clearance, d, of 14 inches on the outside of the curve. Most cars require about 8 inches clearance on the inside of a curve, and a minimum clearance of 8 inches should be allowed for on each side of a straight driveway.

These added widths of driveways required for clearance need not be entirely surfaced like the rest of the driveway, but allowance for them should be made on either side of driveways constructed near trees, retaining walls, or buildings.

In traversing a curve the rear wheels of a car do not follow the paths traversed by the front wheels. They trace paths slightly nearer the center of the curve. The distance between the paths traversed by the outside front and rear wheels when going around a curve is dependent on the radius of the curve and also upon the length of the wheel base. Thus for a car with a 112-inch wheel base traveling on a 30-foot radius curve, the distance, f, is approximately 15 inches, and for a car with a 144-inch wheel base traveling this same curve, f is approximately 24 inches

Another consideration pertinent to widths of curved driveways is the direction of the curve. When driving forward you can follow a curve to either the right or left with equal facility. But when backing up this is not the case. It is much simpler to back around a driveway when the driver is on the inside of the curve, as he can see where he is going. Backing around the outside of a curve, the driver must depend solely on guesswork as the back of the car wholly blocks his view of the driveway.

The gage or width between wheels of the average car is 58 inches. When a car is driven straight forward, two tire tracks are superimposed one over another. However, when driving around a curve, the two outside tire

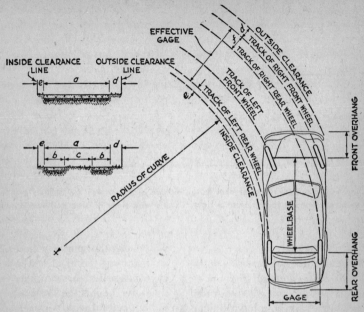

Fig. 8. Illustration of wheel offset *f* and clearances *d* and *e*; distances that must be considered on curbed drives.

tracks are 58 inches (the gage) plus *f*, and this total distance may be called the effective gage, (Fig. 8).

Construction difficulties make it impractical to construct driveways with ribbons wider than 46 inches. And in that case the width between ribbons is only 12 inches and the entire driveway can be surfaced at such a small additional cost that it is wise to do so.

Straight Driveways

Staking out a straight driveway is fairly simple and can be done with a tape measure, a few stakes, and some string. Stakes can be set along the centerline of a drive, along its actual outline, or they can be offset 1 or 2 feet from the outer edges of the drive. The latter is recommended as the stakes need not be disturbed during construction and are thus constantly available as reference points. End stakes are set first, and then intermediate stakes set at measured intervals. True alignment can best be obtained by stretching a string between end stakes. One line is set first and then the other is made parallel to it.

Sometimes perpendicular lines to the outside of a driveway are desired and an easy way to locate them is to construct a right triangle with sides of 3, 4, and 5 feet as illustrated in Fig. 9.

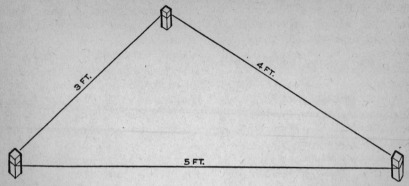

Fig. 9. Sometimes perpendicular lines to the outside of a driveway are desired and an easy way to locate them is to construct a right triangle with sides of 3, 4, and 5 feet as shown above.

Curved Driveways

Curved drives are staked out by locating the center of the curve, swinging arcs of the desired radii, and setting stakes at intervals along these arcs. The center of the curve must be on a perpendicular line at the beginning of the curve.

Driveways that are straight for a distance and then curved need to be wider on the curve than on the straightaway because the effective gage is greater. At the point where the curve begins the driveway needs to be a certain width on one side for the straight part and a greater width on the other for the curve. Rather than having an abrupt increase in width at this point, the drive should flare outward from a point on the

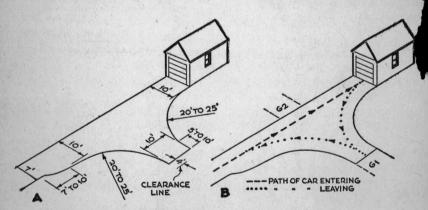

Fig. 10. Design of turning Y suitable for alternate garage locations: A. Ranges in dimensions for short and long cars. B. Paths of car entering and leaving garage. G1 and G2 indicate alternate garage locations.

straight section some 7 to 10 feet from the point of curvature (Fig. 10). This flare will add to the appearance of the driveway and will enable drivers to negotiate the curve more easily.

It is advised that before any construction on a driveway is begun, it be staked out, cleared of any obstructions, and driven over several times to determine whether or not it will be satisfactory. And remember you are going to want to drive over it at night and in stormy weather. If you are going to have to back out over it, you may decide curbs are necessary to guide you, and the best time to build curbs is when you are constructing the driveway.

Turning Areas

If your driveway is long or leads in from a busy street, your best plan may be to provide for a turning area. Backing into a busy street is dangerous and backing out a long driveway will soon become irksome. A turning area may require a little more space and concrete but you may not have

to construct curbs or make your driveway as wide if you do not have to back out.

Figs. 10 to 12 (incl.) illustrate several designs for turning areas. The materials described for use in drive construction can also be used for surfacing turning areas. Paths traced by a car entering or leaving a garage are also shown in these figures. Clearance lines indicated are necessary due to the front and rear overhangs of the car. Ground adjacent to the turning area within the clearance lines should be free from obstructions so that the full turning area can be used, as indicated by the dotted and dashed lines.

The turning areas shown are designed to be easily used with a minimum of turning and backing. Some home owners may be faced with space restrictions that will not conform with the designs or dimensions shown. In such cases more backing and turning may be required to maneuver in and out of the garage.

Some ranges in dimensions shown in Figs. 11 and 12, the sr

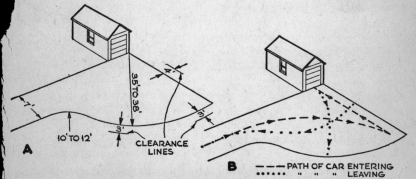

Fig. 11. Design of turning area: A. Ranges in dimensions indicate minimum values for short and long cars. B. Paths of car entering and leaving garage.

dimensions being considered suitable for short cars, and the larger for long cars.

Concrete turning areas should have expansion joints provided at 10-foot intervals in each direction.

Drainage for Driveways

Drainage is not often a serious problem in driveway construction, as most driveways are less than 100 feet in length and drain but a small area. However, care should be taken to insure prompt disposal of water that may run onto and collect on the driveway. This can usually be accomplished by giving the driveway a slight pitch (an inch to 3 or 4 feet) and by diverting surface water that might run onto the drive. Surface draining will adequately dispose of rain water in almost every instance. If underground drainage must be used, a line of 4-inch tile placed 1 foot below the surface will usually suffice. Care should be taken to place sandy soil, gravel, or other porous material over the tile, as clay or other impervious covering will prevent percolation and the proper functioning of the drain.

Driveways that slope downward toward the garage can be drained by installing a drain in the center of the driveway about 4 feet in front of the garage doors, and pipe run from there to the sewer outlet serving the house. The garage floor can also be sloped so that it will drain toward the same outlet.

Some city regulations prohibit carrying outside surface water to a sewer, or limit the area that may be thus drained. So it would be well to consult local authorities or a plumber on this point, as well as about fees and permits for sewer connections.

RIBBON TYPE DRIVEWAY

It is very important when building this type of drive that the sub-base be compact and solid. If it is not, your drive will crack very easily. If the sub-soil is well drained, you do not need any special base, but if it is clayey, you should use a base of gravel or cinders 6 inches thick under the slab. The slab itself should be 5 inches thick unless heavy trucks are going to go over it, in which case it should be 6 inches thick (Fig. 6).

The first step in making the driveway is to lay out the forms. Either 2 x 6, or 2 x 8 inch lumber can be used for the job. The pieces are set on edge and stakes are driven in along the outside to hold them in place. You will need spacers the width of the ribbon placed between the two side forms to hold them the correct distance apart. They should be placed every 6 feet. A ribbon without curbs should be 2 feet wide, but if you plan to include a curb, increase the size to 2½ feet for each ribbon. Fig. 13 shows a simple method of forming the curb. If there are curves in the driveway, the forms for these can be made out of plywood.

You will need an expansion joint in the driveway every 40 feet or so. You should also have one where the driveway joins the apron of the garage or any other concrete or

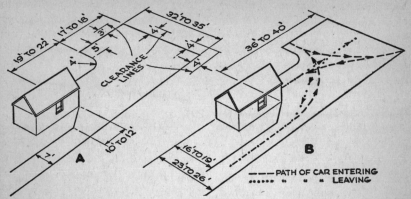

Fig. 12. Alternate design of turning area. A. Ranges in dimensions indicate minimum values for short and long cars. B. Paths of car entering and leaving garage.

masonry work. If expansion joints are not used, there is danger of the concrete's cracking. Expansion joints can be made by placing a strip of asphalt felt between two sections before the fresh concrete is poured, or by leaving a space and filling it later with a bituminous compound (Fig. 14).

Pouring the Concrete

Refer to the Proportioning Table on Page 4 for the correct mixture to use for this job. The entire ribbon is not poured in one operation. Alter-

nate 6-foot sections are poured and then, when the concrete is sufficiently hard, the spacers are removed and the remaining sections are poured. This allows for a slight expansion joint between each 6-foot section. The corners of the sections should be rounded with an edging tool to prevent chipping (Fig. 15).

SLAB TYPE DRIVE

Drives of this sort without curbs should be 6 feet, 10 inches wide

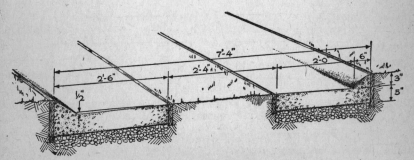

Fig. 13. Ribbon type of driveway, with and without curbs.

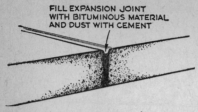

Fig. 14. An expansion joint between two concrete surfaces filled with a bituminous material.

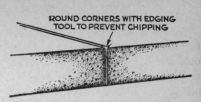

Fig. 15. The edges of adjoining sections of concrete should be rounded off to prevent their chipping.

(Fig. 7). If curbs are to be installed, increase the over-all width of the drive to 7 feet, 4 inches. This allows for two curbs 6 inches thick on each side (Fig. 16).

The same precautions in preparing the sub-base and using a fill in clayey soils apply to this type of drive as to the ribbon drive. The slab type of drive should be 6 inches thick if it is to handle heavy trucks. To allow for proper drainage, it is best to have the top of the concrete slab about 2 inches above the finished grade. The driveway should also be given a slight crown so that water will drain off.

Fig. 16 shows a driveway with such a crown. A board with a hollowed-out edge is used to make the crown. This board is placed with its ends on the top of the form boards and is then worked down along a section of fresh concrete, molding it to the slight crown desired.

The forms for a slab driveway, along with the expansion joints, the mixture, and the method of pouring are just the same as those used for the ribbon type.

When you are working over the surface with a wood float, make certain not to remove the crown.

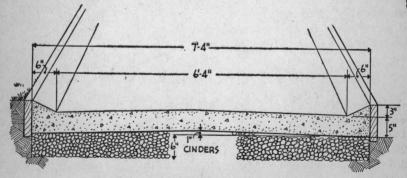

Fig. 16. Curbs on the edges of the driveway will prevent vehicles from running off the concrete strip and damaging the lawn or garden.

FIREPLACE (OUTDOOR)

Nearly anyone can build a satisfactory outdoor fireplace, and the only difference between one built by an expert and one made by a beginner will be in the appearance.

A fireplace can be built of bricks, stone, or poured concrete. Bricks are probably the most popular of these materials because they come in a standard size, are light in weight, easy to work with, and inexpensive. In fact, for an outdoor fireplace even used bricks (secured from a demolished building) may prove entirely satisfactory.

Stones are excellent — provided there is an ample supply nearby. A rather large supply of stones is required to finish a fireplace, so be sure that you will not run out of stones before the work is completed. Stones are of irregular size, and many will require splitting before they can be used. You will need a sledge hammer for that.

Poured concrete makes a good fireplace but requires wood forms. These must be carefully made and the concrete especially well mixed, poured, and cured, so as to withstand the extremes of heat when the fireplace is used.

Materials for Brick Fireplace Foundation
14 cubic feet of cinder or gravel fill
2¾ bags of cement
2/5 cubic yard of gravel or 14 cubic feet of ready-mixed concrete
1/5 cubic yard of sand

Materials for Fireplace
5 bags of cement
4 bags of hydrated lime
1 cubic yard of sand or 25 cu. ft. of ready-mixed mortar
1700 common bricks
200 fire bricks
3 lbs. of fireclay (add 25% portland cement)
2 angle irons 3" x 4" x ¼" x 54"
1 mantle 2" x 10" x 12'

Materials for Cabinets
8 pieces 2" x 8" x 34"
8   "   2" x 4" x 49"
2   "   2" x 4" x 42"
8   "   2" x 4" x 35½"
2   "   2" x 4" x 34"
4   "   2" x 4" x 33¾
4   "   2" x 4" x 22¾"
18 "   1" x 8" x 49"
2   "   1" x 3" x 38"
4   "   1" x 3" x 30"
8 carriage bolts and nuts ¼" x 6"
4 butt hinges 3"
2 barrel bolts 4"
2 strap irons 1/16" x 1"

Building the Fireplace
The size and depth for the excavation, fill, and foundation are given in the Foundation Detail (Shown in Fig. 17). Fine diagonal lines in the drawings indicate common bricks; diagonal cross-hatching indicates fire bricks.

Lay out the first course of bricks as shown in the Foundation Detail. Fill the cavity in the center with gravel and mortar, and then lay one more course. Lay fire bricks along the bottom of the fireplace opening, bringing them flush with the third

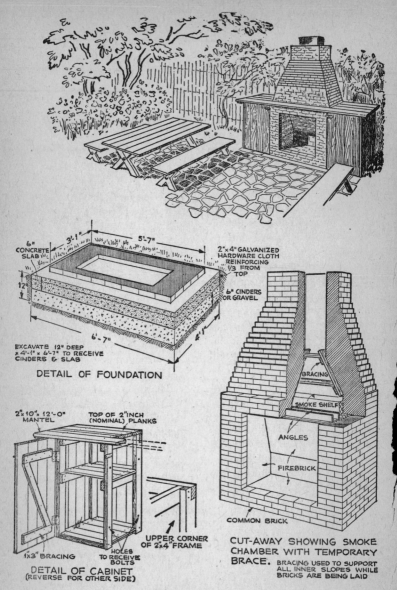

DETAIL OF FOUNDATION

6"
CONCRETE
SLAB

3'-1"

5'-7"

2"x4" GALVANIZED
HARDWARE CLOTH
REINFORCING
1/3 FROM
TOP

12"

6" CINDERS
OR GRAVEL

6'-7"

4'-1"

EXCAVATE 12" DEEP
x 4'-1" x 6'-7" TO RECEIVE
CINDERS & SLAB

2"x10" x 12'-0"
MANTEL

TOP OF 2"INCH
(NOMINAL) PLANKS

UPPER CORNER
OF 2"x4" FRAME

1x3" BRACING

HOLES
TO RECEIVE
BOLTS

DETAIL OF CABINET
(REVERSE FOR OTHER SIDE)

BRACING

SMOKE SHELF

ANGLES

FIREBRICK

COMMON BRICK

CUT-AWAY SHOWING SMOKE
CHAMBER WITH TEMPORARY
BRACE. BRACING USED TO SUPPORT
ALL INNER SLOPES WHILE
BRICKS ARE BEING LAID

Fig. 17. The size and depth for the excavation, fill, and foundation are illustrated above in
the foundation detail. Fine diagonal lines indicate common bricks; diagonal cross-hatching
indicates fire bricks.

thinned with turpentine. Either finish will preserve the wood from decay, though the best practice is to use a decay-resistant wood.

FLOORS (PORCH)

Porch floors may be laid on an earth fill or supported above the ground. When placed at about ground level the slab should be built more or less the same way as a sidewalk, except that aprons should be added on the three sides away from the house. An apron is a cement support about 6 inches thick which extends down into the ground for about 18 inches. The earth under the porch slab should be well settled, and a porous sub-base should be provided. The slab should slope away from the house about ¼ inch per foot to enable water to drain off properly. Sometimes ⅜-inch round rods are set 1 inch from the bottom of the slab, 12 inches on centers both ways (Fig. 19).

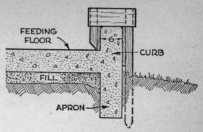

Fig. 19. Curb and apron.

Supports are needed where the slab is elevated or is on a fill more than 12 inches thick. While reinforced girders resting on piers could be used, a much easier method is to build two walls of 8-inch concrete blocks. They eliminate the need for expensive forms and girder reinforcement and are thus cheaper to build when small porches are being added to existing structures. Walls are not needed under the ends of the slab.

Fig. 20 shows details of the construction. Concrete piers 12 inches wide and at least 6 inches deep

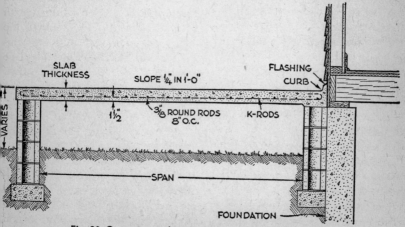

Fig. 20. Concrete porch supported on concrete block walls.

should be poured first. Then the concrete blocks should be cemented in place. After that forms for the slab are built. The accompanying table gives the quantity of reinforcement and the thickness of the slab needed for porches 4 feet to 10 feet wide. Concrete used should be a 1:2½:3½ mix. Do not forget to provide the ¼ inch per foot outside slope.

Reinforcement and Slab Thickness for Supported Porch Floors

Clear span	Slab thickness	Reinforcement Diameter	K-rods Spacing
Feet	Inches	Inches	Inches
4	5	⅜	7½
6	5	⅜	6
8	5½	½	9½
10	6	½	8

Note: Transverse reinforcing rods should be ⅜-inch round rods placed 8 inches on centers.

FOUNDATIONS

A conventional house, built for year-round living in cold climates, with or without a basement, should have a continuous foundation wall of masonry. This not only insures adequate support for the building but makes possible a warm first floor. Masonry used for this type of foundation can be poured concrete or masonry blocks. If masonry blocks are selected, use concrete rather than cinder blocks for below ground level construction.

Excavating a Basement

Should you decide to build a house with a basement, your first job entails the rather extensive chore of excavation. If the foundation top is to be at ground level, you should plan on having at least 7 feet of headroom in the basement. This means that the excavation should be dug 6 inches deeper than this to allow for a 6-inch thick basement floor.

Unless you plan to excavate the area yourself, the hiring of power equipment is recommended. Nowadays it is rarely practical to employ hand labor for this type of work. Even though a power shovel or bulldozer and operator cost considerably more than a day laborer's wages, the work can be done so rapidly that there can still be a considerable financial saving.

Try to personally supervise power shovel or bulldozer work. Unless otherwise directed, most operators will bury all the topsoil under tons of gravel and clay. Consequently, when you begin landscaping you'll either have to buy topsoil or uncover that which was buried. Have the operator dump all topsoil (usually running to a depth of about 1 foot) in a predetermined area.

Area to be Excavated

The use of single or double form will help to determine the area to be excavated. If the soil is well packed, well drained, and you plan to use poured concrete, it may be possible to use the sides of the excavation as outside forms. In this case, the excavation should be plotted and dug to exact dimensions.

If the soil is not well drained, draintile should be laid along the outside base of the foundation to facilitate getting proper drainage and a dry basement. In this case the excavation will have to be made about 2 feet wider and double forms will be needed. When using masonry blocks allow sufficient room to work on the outside face of the wall.

Footings

Footings are the base that support foundation walls as well as the weight of the entire house. They must be used with all types of foundations, including piers. Where normal soil conditions exist, footings should be as deep as foundation walls are wide, and twice their width. For example, if the foundation walls are to be 10 inches thick, the footings should be 10 inches deep and 20 inches wide. The foundation wall is then centered so that the footing projects 5 inches on either side of it.

Footings should be made of poured concrete. They must extend below the frost line because frost penetration might result in heaving up and cracking of the foundation wall. It is always a wise precaution to check with local builders or county agricultural agents because safe depth varies to a great extent according to different types of soils. Dry soils ordinarily do not heave when freezing, but damp clay may heave enough to cause serious damage to the building.

In regions where there is little frost, set footings below the topsoil on firm ground because if they are placed close to the surface rodents may burrow under them and wind, rains or floods may erode the soil from beneath causing the building to

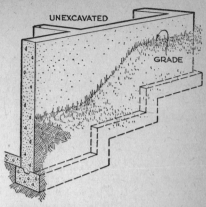

Fig. 21. Method of stepping wall footings.

settle. In some localities the firm soil is a relatively thin layer over soft ground. If the firm soil is penetrated, it is virtually impossible to secure a good footing. Under such conditions shallow footings may be protected from erosion by banking the soil against the foundations. The fill requires sodding and protection from erosion caused by the drip from the roof, which should be reduced with gutters and downspouts.

All footings of buildings are preferably set on the same type of soil and must be level though not necessarily at the same elevation. Where the ground slopes or where there is a basement under only a portion of the building, step the footing down gradually to avoid undermining the higher portion (Fig. 21).

The ratio in which the stepping can be done safely varies with the type of soil, but for average conditions a vertical rise, V, of not more than 2 feet in a horizontal distance, H, of 4 feet is generally satisfactory.

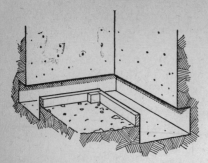

Fig. 22. Excavation cut back to make an earth form for the footing. A 2 x 4" on edge along the inside edge of the cut serves as a form for the top of the footing and also as a means of anchoring the base of the foundation forms in place.

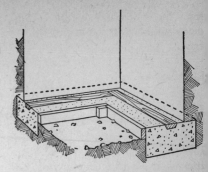

Fig. 23. A recess can be made in the footing by setting a beveled and greased 2 x 4" into the concrete before it is hard. This is removed before the foundation forms are installed.

Digging the Footing

In many cases you will not need footing forms; the sides of the trench dug for them will serve the purpose. The trench should be dug by hand and should be as square as possible. Footings poured into a round bottom trench will not have the carrying capacity of those with a square even base.

If the exterior walls of the excavation are to serve as outside forms for the foundation wall, it will be necessary to undercut into this wall for a distance of 5 inches for the footing. The best way of doing this is to place a 2 by 4 on edge 15 inches from the wall of the excavation. Drive stakes along the inside of this board to hold it securely in place. Be sure that it is level because it will serve as a top to the form for the footing. Proceed to undercut into the excavation for 5 inches and dig the trench (Fig. 22).

Make the sides and the bottom of the trench as clean as possible. If the

soil is dry and tends to crumble, dampen it lightly before you pour the footings.

Footings should be poured in one operation. The usual mix is 1 part cement, 3.75 parts sand, and 5 parts gravel. The method of surfacing the top of the footings will depend on the materials that you are going to use for the foundation wall. If you plan to use masonry blocks, the top of the footing should be level and smooth. If you are going to use poured concrete, a key slot should be made in the footing to insure proper bond between footing and foundation. This key can be made by forcing a bevelled 2 by 4 into the middle of the concrete before it has set. Grease the 2 by 4 before insertion so that it can easily be removed (Fig. 23).

Do not allow the footings to extend above the 2 x 4's serving as inner forms. These can later be used to attach the foundation forms in place.

Keep the fresh concrete covered and damp until it has set and cured properly.

Foundation Forms

As soon as the footings are placed and have set, the work of assembling the foundation forms can get underway. These forms may be built of sheathing boards or plywood. The framework for them can be made out of 2 by 4's and 2 by 6's. Because most of the lumber needed can be re-used, eliminate needless cutting. Use short lengths for the framework and allow them to extend beyond the top of the forms rather than cut them to exact size. It is advisable to use special concrete-form nails with two heads, as these can be removed easily without damage to the wood. You can either build the forms in sections for later assemblage or build them all as one unit.

Attaching the Form Base

There are several ways to attach the base of the forms in place. If you

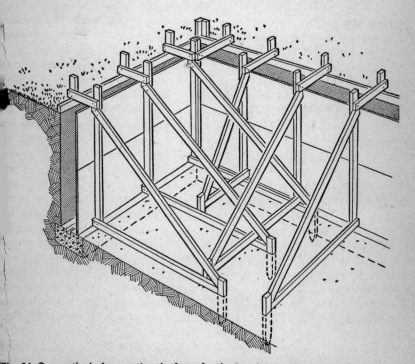

Fig. 24. One method of supporting the forms for the foundations. The detail shows a 2" x 4" spiked to the top of the footing form. The siding used for the forms overhangs the form framework enough so it will hook behind this 2" x 4".

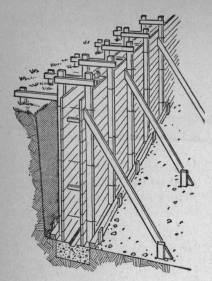

Fig. 25. Another method of bracing the forms for the foundations. A length of 2 x 4" on edge along the base serves to hold the lower portion of the form in place. Diagonal braces support the upper portion.

used a 2 x 4 as a form top for the footing, this can serve as a nailing b̲a̲s̲ ̲for the sole plate. See detail in Fig. 24.

Place a 2 x 4 or 2 x 6 down along the footing; allow the edge to overlap the 2 x 4 staked to the ground. Spike the two together and then use the sole plate to toe-nail the vertical framework. When the time arrives to attach the form sheathing, be sure that the first course extends far enough so that its lower edge can be nailed to this base plate as well as to the vertical studding.

If the footings come just level with the ground, a 2 by 4 or 2 by 6 can be placed on edge on the outside of the footings and held in place by

stakes driven into the ground. The studding for the forms is placed inside of this plate and nailed (Fig. 24).

Bracing the Forms

Poured concrete exerts tremendous pressures. Forms for the foundation should be solidly constructed, therefore, and adequately braced to withstand displacement by the weight of the concrete. The proper method of bracing forms is shown in Figs. 24 and 25.

Note that outside as well as inside forms are illustrated. Whether or not outside forms are needed will depend on local soil conditions. Dry soil that crumbles easily will not provide a satisfactory substitute outside form. It will absorb moisture from the fresh concrete and if sufficient particles enter the concrete mix during the pouring operation, weak spots, and possible leaks in the wall may result.

Studding

Studding for the forms should be spaced no more than 18 inches on center. Apply the sheathing on the inside of the studding so that the weight of the concrete will not force it out of position, as would be the case if it were applied on the outside. If inside and outside forms are used 1 by 2-inch spacer blocks should be used to keep the forms equi-distant. Inside and outside studding forms should be tied together with No. 10 wire to prevent spreading. Install the spacers first so that, as the wire is tightened, the forms will not be pulled together.

Foundation Openings

Fig 26 shows the forms needed for a basement outside stair well. Walls around the stair well do not have to be as thick as those for the foundation wall. Bevelled cleats should be attached to the forms used to frame the basement door (as shown in the illustration) so that, after the concrete is hard, the cleats, which remain embedded in the concrete, can be used to fasten the door frame in place. For these cleats, use wood treated to resist decay and insects.

Proposed window openings should be cut in the forms and framed. The frames may be built out of wood, or you can purchase metal ones intended for use with metal window sashes (Fig. 27). Since these windows will be below or, at best, near ground level, you will need wells around them on the outside. The wells can be dug by hand; they can be made of poured concrete or metal. Concrete window wells should extend at least 18 inches below the bottom of the window opening and they should be 6 inches thick. Do not cement the

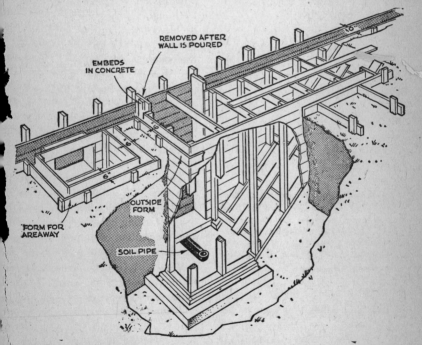

Fig. 26. Forms for the basement stair well should be constructed at the same time as those for the foundation walls. Note the detail of the doorway into the basement. Beveled cleats are embedded into the concrete and will serve as a nailing base for the basement doorway frame. The area-way around the basement window should extend for at least 18" below the bottom of the window opening.

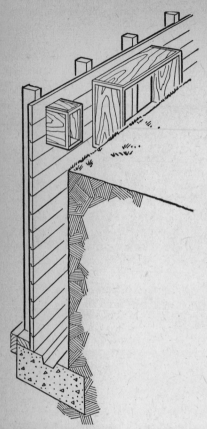

Fig. 27. A pocket for the girder and openings for basement windows must be built into the form. The frame for the window opening has beveled cleats on the sides which remain in the concrete after the forms are removed and serve as a nailing base for the window frames.

well bottoms unless you plan to include a drain.

Provision for girder pockets and additional openings for pipes etc., should be allowed for. The inside of wood forms should be greased to permit easier removal. However, wood forms should not be greased if you plan to paint or treat the foundation wall.

Pouring Foundation Walls

A suitable mix for a poured concrete foundation can be found on the chart on Page 4. It is rarely practical to mix concrete for such a project by hand, as the best results for obtaining a waterproof foundation demand that the concrete be poured in one continuous operation.

There are two ways that this can be done. Ready-mixed concrete which is delivered ready to pour can be bought, or a concrete mixer can be hired. In either case have enough extra help available to pour and tamp the concrete into the forms. Remember that fresh concrete should be poured approximately 30 minutes after the dry cement and sand have been mixed. Concrete should never be poured when the temperature is less than 40° unless special precautions are taken.

The footing should be dampened and sprinkled with dry cement before the first layer is poured. This will insure a strong bond between footing and foundation wall. The concrete should be placed in 6-inch layers and it should be tamped and spaded to eliminate air pockets. Never spade or tamp the concrete too much as this will cause the aggregate to rise to the top.

Remove the spacer blocks as the concrete is poured. Be particularly careful to work the concrete around windows and other openings, as a faulty job can create problems.

Reinforcement

Reinforcements placed at the corners of concrete foundations help to prevent cracks which often develop at wall intersections. Half-inch rods 6 feet long are usually bent into ells and laid in the center of the wall at each 8 inches of height so that one leg of each projects into the end wall and the other into the side wall. Where a long or high concrete wall is exposed to temperature changes special reinforcement may be advisable.

Anchor Bolts

Anchor bolts, as their name implies, are intended to lock the superstructure of a building to the foundation wall. Frame buildings must be anchored to continuous foundation walls by ⅝- or ¾-inch bolts spaced 6 to 8 feet apart. Bolts extending less than 18 inches into concrete walls and 2 to 3 feet into concrete block wall are likely to be pulled out.

Anchor bolts may be installed after the concrete has been allowed to set for a short time, or they can be suspended in spacer strips nailed at the proper interval.

After the anchor bolts are installed, the concrete top surface should be smoothed off and it should be covered with damp burlap, tar paper, or boards to save the surface from damage and to keep the concrete from drying too rapidly.

Curing

Allow the concrete at least a week to set and cure before stripping off the forms. Be careful when you dismantle the forms so as not to damage the wood for further use. Knock off any bits of dry concrete that may cling to them, and store the boards where they will be handy for further use.

GARAGE OF CONCRETE BLOCK

Concrete blocks provide a most workable means for a one-man construction project. The nominal 8 x 8 x 16-inch blocks are ideally suited for garage construction as they can be competently handled by most amateurs after a short time. Corner blocks with one square end, half blocks which facilitate building the wall with staggered vertical joints, and lintels for framing the top of windows are available (Fig. 28).

Cinder Blocks

These may be used instead of concrete blocks. The only difference in manufacture is that concrete blocks are made of portland cement, sand and crushed stone, while in cinder blocks, cinders replace the crushed stone. Although lacking the great strength of concrete blocks, cinder blocks are nevertheless very durable and have greater sound-absorption qualities.

Locating the Garage

Carefully check building regulations as to placement and construction of your garage. Moreover, the site should be well drained and easily approached. See material on *Driveways*.

Planning Factors

The garage plans illustrated in Fig. 29 are not given as final work drawings and should not be used as such. They are intended to be of help in the preparation of exact plans which

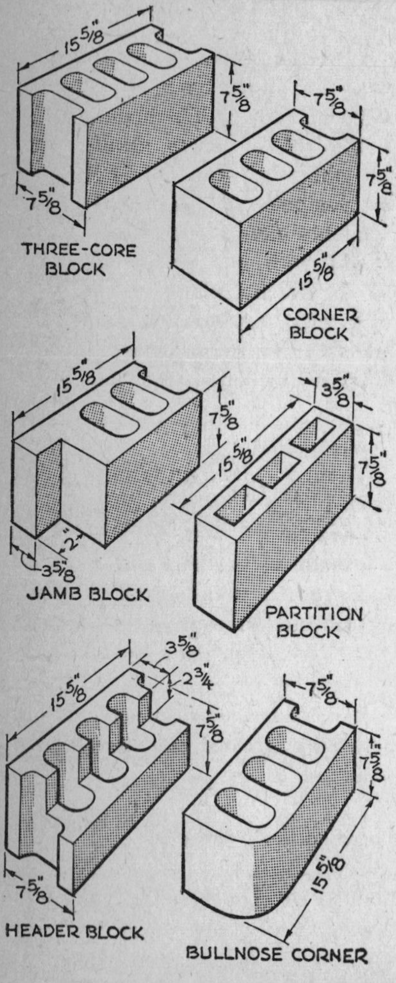

Fig. 28. Common shapes and sizes of concrete masonry units.

should conform to local conditions and legal requirements.

Select the type of door you plan to install before you draw up your plans. Certain doors require special fittings if they are to work properly. Provisions for them must be included in your building specifications. Most manufacturers will gladly furnish on request illustrated literature showing proper construction details.

Consider the advantages of building a two-car garage, half of which can be rented until the time you become a two-car family. The money derived in the form of rent over a period of years will amply repay the additional expenditure as well as any maintenance costs that may accrue. Garage plans may also include a workshop area, and it is always wise to allot a room for storing garden tools, ladders, and children's toys.

Once you have a set of plans, stake out the proposed garage walls on the site. Allow ⅜-inch space between blocks for mortar joints. The foregoing procedure will enable you to determine whether or not you will need to cut any blocks to size.

Since you will undoubtedly find working with standard whole-or-half blocks easier, your dimensions can be readily scaled at this stage to eliminate cutting. For additional convenience, plan the distances of window and door openings, as well as the distances between them, in multiples of 8 inches.

Roofs

As a rule, the type of roof selected for the garage should conform with that of your home. For example, if your house has a hip roof, your garage should also have a hip roof.

When constructing a garage with a gable roof, it is wise for the amateur to limit concrete block construction

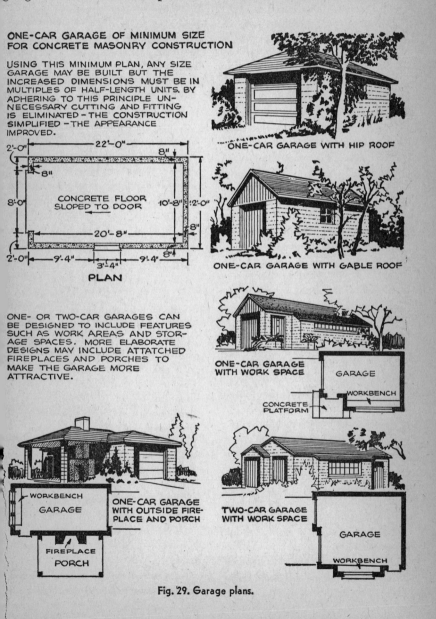

ONE-CAR GARAGE OF MINIMUM SIZE FOR CONCRETE MASONRY CONSTRUCTION

USING THIS MINIMUM PLAN, ANY SIZE GARAGE MAY BE BUILT BUT THE INCREASED DIMENSIONS MUST BE IN MULTIPLES OF HALF-LENGTH UNITS. BY ADHERING TO THIS PRINCIPLE UN-NECESSARY CUTTING AND FITTING IS ELIMINATED – THE CONSTRUCTION SIMPLIFIED – THE APPEARANCE IMPROVED.

CONCRETE FLOOR SLOPED TO DOOR

PLAN

ONE-CAR GARAGE WITH HIP ROOF

ONE-CAR GARAGE WITH GABLE ROOF

ONE- OR TWO-CAR GARAGES CAN BE DESIGNED TO INCLUDE FEATURES SUCH AS WORK AREAS AND STOR-AGE SPACES. MORE ELABORATE DESIGNS MAY INCLUDE ATTATCHED FIREPLACES AND PORCHES TO MAKE THE GARAGE MORE ATTRACTIVE.

ONE-CAR GARAGE WITH WORK SPACE

GARAGE

WORKBENCH

CONCRETE PLATFORM

WORKBENCH

GARAGE

ONE-CAR GARAGE WITH OUTSIDE FIRE-PLACE AND PORCH

FIREPLACE

PORCH

TWO-CAR GARAGE WITH WORK SPACE

GARAGE

WORKBENCH

Fig. 29. Garage plans.

to the square portions of the wall. The triangular upper sections of the masonry walls should be built with some other material. Although concrete blocks can be angled with a cold chisel and a mason's hammer, an inexperienced person may find the process difficult.

Footings and Foundation

Every concrete block wall must have a firm base to support it. Local weather conditions will determine the type of footing and foundation needed. Only where there is no danger of frost can the type of footing-foundation shown in Fig. 30 be used.

In all other areas it will be necessary to install a footing below the frost line, and a foundation wall. Since the size of the footing is determined by the width of the foundation wall to be installed, the width for a concrete block foundation wall should be 8 inches deep ... 6 inches wide.

The footing should be of poured concrete and it should be square and straight. If poured concrete is chosen for the foundation wall the footing should be keyed. For complete information about footings and foundations refer to the material on *Foundations*.

Flooring

The garage floor may be laid before or after the concrete block walls are erected. The floor surface should be 6 inches above grade and the floor should rest on 6 inches of compacted subgrade. It should be 4 inches thick unless it is going to be subjected to abnormal tonnage. In this instance the flooring thickness should be increased to 6 inches.

Whenever a foundation wall is used, an expansion joint must be installed around the entire inside perimeter. The expansion joint may consist of two thicknesses of roofing felt or a ½-inch premolded expansion joint.

The flooring should slope toward and extend approximately 3 feet beyond the garage door to form an apron. Where the apron joins the drive a ½-inch expansion joint must also be included. Examine Fig. 30, and note the door entrance details.

Concrete Block Construction

Store concrete blocks in a dry place until they are installed. Check the footing to make sure that it is straight and stretch chalk lines to serve as guides in building the corners. Use a chalk line stretched between corners as shown in Fig. 31(2) to serve as guides in building the walls.

A suitable mix for concrete block mortar can be made from 1 part cement to 2 parts of clean fine sand. Add enough water to this mixture to produce a workable plastic mass. Do not make more mortar than you can use in 30 minutes. The normal mortar joint, horizontal and vertical, is about ⅜ inch.

For the first course of block, place mortar the full width of the block wall as shown in Fig. 31(1). For subsequent courses place the mortar in a double row on the block already laid. The method of placing the mortar illustrated in Figs. 31(3) and

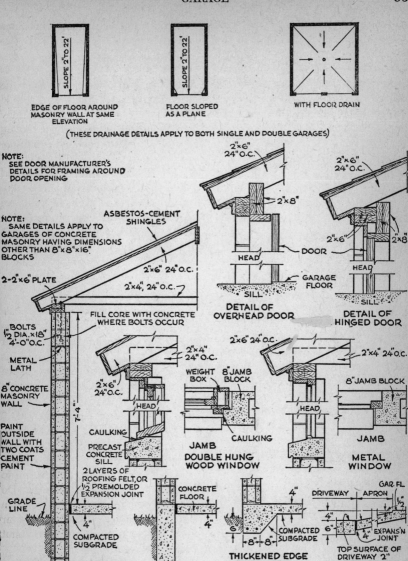

SLOPE 2' TO 22'

EDGE OF FLOOR AROUND
MASONRY WALL AT SAME
ELEVATION

SLOPE 2' TO 22'

FLOOR SLOPED
AS A PLANE

WITH FLOOR DRAIN

(THESE DRAINAGE DETAILS APPLY TO BOTH SINGLE AND DOUBLE GARAGES)

NOTE:
SEE DOOR MANUFACTURER'S
DETAILS FOR FRAMING AROUND
DOOR OPENING

NOTE:
SAME DETAILS APPLY TO
GARAGES OF CONCRETE
MASONRY HAVING DIMENSIONS
OTHER THAN 8"x8"x16"
BLOCKS

ASBESTOS-CEMENT
SHINGLES

2"x6" 24" O.C.

2"x4", 24" O.C.

2-2"x6" PLATE

FILL CORE WITH CONCRETE
WHERE BOLTS OCCUR

BOLTS
½ DIA.x18"
4'-0"O.C.

METAL
LATH

8" CONCRETE
MASONRY
WALL

PAINT
OUTSIDE
WALL WITH
TWO COATS
CEMENT
PAINT

7'-4"

CAULKING

PRECAST
CONCRETE
SILL

2 LAYERS OF
ROOFING FELT, OR
½ PREMOLDED
EXPANSION JOINT

GRADE
LINE

4"

COMPACTED
SUBGRADE

CONCRETE
FOOTING

8"

16"

WALL SECTION WITH
CONCRETE MASONRY
FOUNDATION

2"x6"
24" O.C.

2"x8"

HEAD

DOOR

GARAGE
FLOOR

SILL

DETAIL OF
OVERHEAD DOOR

2"x6"
24" O.C.

2"x6"   2"x8"

HEAD

SILL

DETAIL OF
HINGED DOOR

2"x4"
24" O.C.

2"x6"
24" O.C.

HEAD

WEIGHT
BOX

8" JAMB
BLOCK

CAULKING

JAMB
DOUBLE HUNG
WOOD WINDOW

2"x6" 24" O.C.

2"x4" 24"O.C.

HEAD

8" JAMB BLOCK

JAMB
METAL
WINDOW

CONCRETE
FLOOR

8"

4"

8" 8"

4"

6"

COMPACTED
SUBGRADE

THICKENED EDGE
FLOOR SLAB
FOUNDATION
(USED ONLY WHERE
THERE IS NO FROST
UPHEAVAL)

DRIVEWAY

GAR. FL

APRON

4"

4"

6"

EXPANS'N
JOINT

TOP SURFACE OF
DRIVEWAY 2"
ABOVE GRADE

DETAIL OF GARAGE
FLOOR AT ENTRANCE

CONCRETE
FOOTING

8"

BELOW FROST AND
ON FIRM SOIL

¾ DIA. BAR

8"

CAST-IN-PLACE
FOUNDATION

Fig. 30. Construction details for concrete masonry garages.

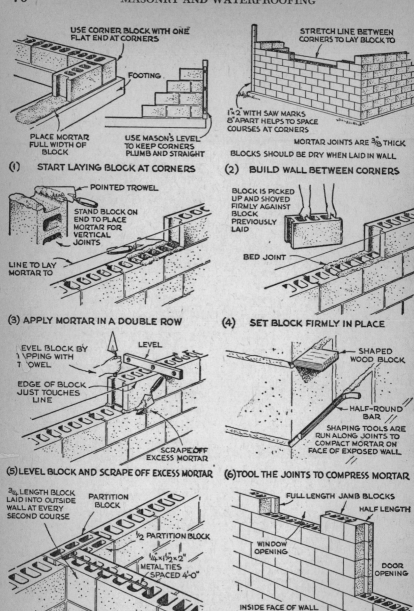

USE CORNER BLOCK WITH ONE FLAT END AT CORNERS

FOOTING

PLACE MORTAR FULL WIDTH OF BLOCK

USE MASON'S LEVEL TO KEEP CORNERS PLUMB AND STRAIGHT

(1)   START LAYING BLOCK AT CORNERS

STRETCH LINE BETWEEN CORNERS TO LAY BLOCK TO

1"x2 WITH SAW MARKS 8" APART HELPS TO SPACE COURSES AT CORNERS

MORTAR JOINTS ARE 3/8" THICK

BLOCKS SHOULD BE DRY WHEN LAID IN WALL

(2)   BUILD WALL BETWEEN CORNERS

POINTED TROWEL

STAND BLOCK ON END TO PLACE MORTAR FOR VERTICAL JOINTS

LINE TO LAY MORTAR TO

(3) APPLY MORTAR IN A DOUBLE ROW

BLOCK IS PICKED UP AND SHOVED FIRMLY AGAINST BLOCK PREVIOUSLY LAID

BED JOINT

(4)   SET BLOCK FIRMLY IN PLACE

LEVEL BLOCK BY TAPPING WITH TROWEL

LEVEL

EDGE OF BLOCK JUST TOUCHES LINE

SCRAPE OFF EXCESS MORTAR

(5) LEVEL BLOCK AND SCRAPE OFF EXCESS MORTAR

SHAPED WOOD BLOCK

HALF-ROUND BAR

SHAPING TOOLS ARE RUN ALONG JOINTS TO COMPACT MORTAR ON FACE OF EXPOSED WALL

(6) TOOL THE JOINTS TO COMPRESS MORTAR

3/4 LENGTH BLOCK LAID INTO OUTSIDE WALL AT EVERY SECOND COURSE

PARTITION BLOCK

1/2 PARTITION BLOCK

1/4"x1 1/2"x2" METAL TIES SPACED 4'-0"

(7) BUILD PARTITION WALLS INTO OUTSIDE WALLS

FULL LENGTH JAMB BLOCKS

HALF LENGTH

WINDOW OPENING

DOOR OPENING

INSIDE FACE OF WALL

(8) JAMB BLOCKS AT DOOR AND WINDOW

Fig. 31. Methods illustrated above will produce strong, durable concrete block walls.

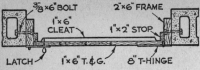

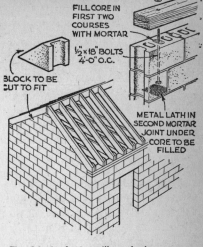

Fig. 32. A method of building door frames which is suitable for most service buildings.

31(4) is called "face shell bedding."

Butter one end of the block with mortar and shove it firmly against the unit previously placed, Fig. 31(5). Level and plumb the block and scrape off the excess mortar squeezed out between the joints.

After the mortar has become quite stiff run a pointing tool of the type shown in Fig. 31(6) along the mortar joints. This compacts the mortar and helps to make tight strong joints. To give vertical joints the same texture as the concrete blocks, they should be rubbed with a piece of carpet, cork, or some other rough material.

Where cross wall and partitions intersect outside walls, use the type of construction shown in Fig. 31(7). The jamb block is used for door frames, and for both wood and steel

Fig. 34. Anchoring sills and plates to concrete masonry walls by bolts.

window frames as shown in Fig. 31 (8). After the masonry and other construction work is completed, install door and window frames. Small door openings can be framed with 2 by 6-inch material as shown in Fig. 32. Use corner block instead of recessed jamb block for the side of such openings.

Sills and Lintels

Concrete sills and lintels can be cast in place or they can be purchased. Lintels are used to span openings over windows and doors. They support the wall and roof over the openings. Two ⅜-inch rods are used for lintels carrying wall loads over openings less than 8 feet wide. Where lintels are required to carry more than a wall load, you should seek the advice of an architect.

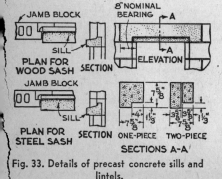

Fig. 33. Details of precast concrete sills and lintels.

Two types of sills are commonly used. One is for metal windows and has a raised shoulder to support the window frame. The other type is for wood frame windows. Both types project over the face of the wall for about 1 inch and have a groove or drip on the underside of the overhang so that water running off the sill will fall free and not run down the face of the wall possibly staining it (Fig. 33).

Plate Level Construction

The usual method of fastening the plate is shown in Fig. 34. Mortar ½ by 18-inch bolts into the block at 4-foot intervals. Place metal lath or screen in the second mortar joint under the core to be filled. This supports the bolt as well as the mortar poured into the core. Two thicknesses of 2 by 6 or 2 by 8-inch planks are bolted down for the plate. The walls should always be braced at plate level.

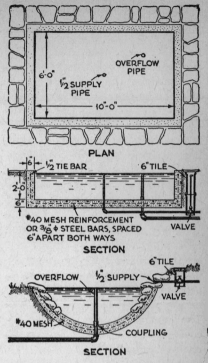

Fig. 35. Either of these two concrete pools can be easily built by the home handyman.

POOL (GARDEN)

A garden pool will greatly enhance the attractiveness of a garden. You can keep fish in it or not as you see fit. Build it of watertight concrete which is reinforced so it will not crack from the pressure of the water or the soil around it. Fig. 35 gives plans for a couple of types of pools. Once the essentials discussed have been incorporated into a pool, any number of variations can be made to suit your particular inclinations.

In selecting a site for the pool, keep in mind that it will have to be drained from time to time, and regardless of whether you keep fish in it or not the water will need to be changed. Therefore it might be well to have it situated near the house rather than at the far end of your property. The best and easiest way of draining the pool is to put down a drain pipe at the bottom of the pool, and run it to some point lower than the lowest portion of the pool. If no drain pipe is installed, the pool will have to be emptied by hand, and while this is not difficult with small pools, it requires a considerable amount of work to drain larger pools in this fashion.

Dig out the necessary amount of earth and set the drain pipe in place. The opening of the drain pipe should be at the lowest point in the pool. A very effective way of combining an overflow pipe with a drain pipe is to attach a coupling to the drain pipe so that the coupling is almost covered by the concrete bottom of the pool. Screw a length of pipe into the coupling, and this pipe will act as an overflow. When draining the pool, unscrew the overflow pipe, and the water will flow out through the coupling.

If the soil is solid, only inside forms will be required; if it is loose, both outside and inside forms will be needed. To reinforce the concrete, use 40-lb. mesh wire, placed in the middle of the 6-inch thick concrete. The faces of the forms should be covered with oil so that they can be removed easily.

Mix the concrete in proportions of 1:2¼:3 and take great pains that the proportions are exactly right. To prevent seams in the concrete, do all the pouring in a continuous operation. Shovel in about 8 inches of concrete and spade it so that it becomes a well-packed mass. Then shovel in another batch and continue until the entire pool has been completed. Keep fresh concrete moist and covered for a week or ten days until it has set. Do not try to remove the forms for several days.

Small pools of course can be filled with a garden hose, but a ½-inch water line connected to the house plumbing system is more convenient. Fig. 35 shows two methods of providing such lines. The inlet line should be fitted with a valve so that the flow of water can be easily controlled from a point near the pool.

The alkali that is present in new concrete will kill fish. It is possible to check the amount of alkali in the water with pink litmus paper, obtainable at a drug store. If the paper turns blue when placed in the water, it is not safe for fish. Change the water at weekly intervals until pink litmus paper remains pink. Then fish can be placed in the pool.

SHUFFLEBOARD COURT

Shuffleboard, long established as the most popular of shipboard sports, can be played in your backyard or alleyway. Construction of the smooth-surfaced 52 x 6-foot court differs slightly from a well-made sidewalk (Fig. 36).

A level site should be selected. If the area is poorly drained, a 6-inch base of well-compacted coarse gravel or cinders will be needed.

The ground should be excavated to a uniform depth and the dug-out area should be rolled or tamped firm and level. A wooden form with inside dimensions of 52 feet x 6 feet can be tacked to stakes lining the perimeter of the trench. All sides of the form must be level and parallel.

The concrete should be placed in two layers. The 3-inch-thick base layer should be made with 1 part cement, 2¼ parts of clean coarse sand, and 3 parts crushed stone or gravel. Sand should range in size from fine grains to particles ¼ inch in size,

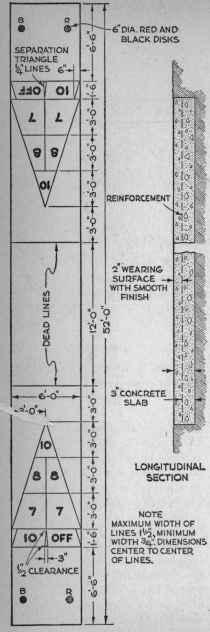

Fig. 36. Shuffleboard court.

while the stone or gravel should consist of particles ranging between ¼ and 1 inch. The concrete should be thoroughly mixed with not more than 6 gallons of water per sack of cement. The base course should be struck off to grade after which a reinforcement consisting of expanded metal or wire mesh, weighing not less than 60 pounds per 100 square feet, should be put down.

Playing Layer

The wearing or playing layer should be mixed and placed within 45 minutes after the base layer is struck off. If colored concrete is desired, a commercial pure mineral oxide pigment may be added. The coloring materials added should not exceed 10 per cent of the weight of the cement. The full coloring value of color pigment can only be obtained by using white cement and white sand for the top layer. Pigment, aggregate, and cement should be mixed dry before water is added.

The playing layer should be 2 inches thick and should consist of 1 part cement, 1 part of clean or white sand, and 1¾ parts of fine crushed stone or gravel. The stone or gravel should grade from ⅛ to ⅜ inch in size. This layer should be made with not more than from 4½ to 5 gallons of water per sack of cement. The concrete should be fairly stiff and it should require some tamping to settle it in place.

After the wearing layer is placed it should carefully be brought to grade with a straight edge. It should then be compacted with a wood float and again tested with a straight edge to detect high and low spots which should be eliminated. A limited amount of steel trowelling should only be started after the concrete has hardened sufficiently to prevent excess fine material from working to the surface. After the concrete has further hardened, it should be carefully hand troweled until the desired smooth finish is attained.

Curing

This step is one of the most important operations in the construction of a shuffleboard court. The finished surface must be kept wet for a period of 7 days. Water should be applied directly to the surface as soon as the concrete is hard enough to withstand marring by the process.

The concrete may be kept wet by any of the following methods. The most satisfactory process would be to build earthen dikes around the edge of the court and keep them filled with water for the required period. Another method of curing is to cover the concrete with a 2-inch layer of clean sand, or a layer of burlap, keeping the covering constantly wet by sprinkling for the 7-day period.

Curing is most important, for if the concrete is allowed to dry too rapidly at the surface, the mixing water needed for hardening will evaporate, and cause surface checking or cracks. Premature drying will also cause the surface to dust under service.

After the court has cured for the prescribed period it should be allowed to dry for 4 or 5 days. The playing lines can then be painted on the surface.

Marking the Court

A high quality paint made with an oil or varnish base is satisfactory for use on concrete surfaces. For new construction (less than 6 months old), a zinc sulphate wash consisting of 3 pounds of crystal per gallon of water should be applied to the surface to be painted. At least 48 hours should be allowed for the zinc sulphate treatment to dry after it is applied. Any crystals that appear on the surface should be brushed off before painting.

If a waxed surface is desired, a treatment with paraffin wax dissolved in turpentine, followed by a coating of powdered wax well rubbed in, will give excellent results.

SIDEWALKS

Sidewalks made of properly proportioned concrete fulfill all the essentials of any good footway. They withstand the ravages of traffic and time, offer eye appeal, and are easy to sweep or shovel.

Many communities have set regulations regarding the construction of public sidewalks. These regulations must be followed.

Width

Use should determine the width of any walk not specifically dictated by law. Main pathways from the street to the house entrance should be wide; 4 to 5 feet is usually a good width. Those on the side or rear of the house may vary from 1½ to 3 feet.

Drainage

If the soil is not well drained naturally, a sub-base of well-compacted, clean coarse gravel, or clean cinders must be provided. A good sub-base should be about 6 inches thick. It should be rolled or tapped firm to offer a solid base for the concrete, and should be wetted before the concrete is poured.

Thickness

If the sidewalk is to be used only as a walk, 4 inches of concrete should be sufficient, but if a heavy vehicle—such as a truck delivering coal—is likely to be driven over it, the thickness should be 6 inches.

Forms

Side forms can be made of 2 x 4's or 2 x 6's and they can be held in place by stakes. The top edges of the forms will later serve as guides in leveling off the concrete. Always build walks about 2 inches above

grade so that they will be well drained. In building a 6-inch-thick walk, therefore, the area that is to be concreted will have to be excavated to a depth of 4 inches plus the thickness of the fill. The walk should be sloped toward one side for drainage; a pitch of from ¼ to ½ inch is satisfactory (Fig 37).

Walks are best built in one-course construction. This means that the full thickness of concrete is poured at one time using the same mixture throughout.

Expansion joints

To allow for the expansion and contraction of cement, walks should be divided at 4- to 6-foot intervals, with partition strips placed at right angles to the side form. Every other section should be concreted. After these have hardened enough to be self-sustaining, the cross strips are removed and the remaining slabs placed.

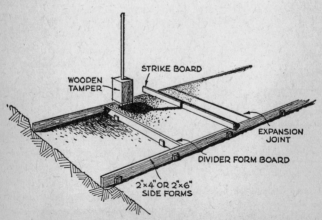

Fig. 37. A concrete sidewalk under construction.

A ½-inch expansion joint will have to be included for every 50 feet of sidewalk being constructed. This can be made by inserting a board ½ inch thick between adjacent sections. The board should be removed when the concrete is sufficiently hard to permit its removal without damaging the edges. The joint between sections may be filled with a bituminous material or dusted with cement.

If you wish to build the walk in consecutive sequence, place strips of tarred felt against the division or header boards. When the header boards are removed, these strips, which should extend across the entire walk for its full depth, remain permanently in position assuring a definite joint between sections. Concrete is placed on both sides of the header board. When the board is removed, the pressure of concrete from both sides holds the tarred felt vertically.

The proper mixture of concrete to use will be found in the Proportion-ing Table on Page 4. Familiarize yourself with the instructions for proportioning, placing and curing. These can be found in Chapter 1.

The concrete mixture, when of the right plasticity, can easily be leveled off by a strikeboard resting on the edges of the side forms. Pass the strikeboard across the forms in a saw-like motion. Several hours later the concrete should be finished with a wood float to produce an even, gritty surface, and all edges should be rounded with a cement finisher's edging tool.

STEPS

Steps vary somewhat depending on the location and number needed. There are two quite different ways of building them. When only three or four steps are needed, as from low porch or doorway to the ground, or up a slight incline in the grounds, solid steps can be poured as shown in Fig. 38. In this case building the form is simple, a large rectangle or square at the bottom, and smaller ones above it, form the steps.

The vertical height or face of a step is called the "riser," and the horizontal surface the "tread." The other method of building concrete steps is to cast the risers and treads on an inclined slab, the thickness of which depends on the span or method of support.

When the slab rests on solid earth or on an earth fill between concrete or other masonry walls and there are but three or four steps from 3 to 4 feet wide, a 4-inch slab is sufficient;

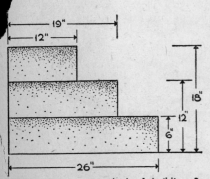

Fig. 38. An easy method of building 3 cement steps. Build form for the bottom step, pour it, and after it has set build the form for the second, etc.

Fig. 39. Steps supported on earth with parts of forms cut away to show construction.

but for wider or longer flights the slab should be 6 inches or more in thickness. Two arrangements of forms are illustrated in Fig. 39. Steps that do not rest on solid earth or fill must be reinforced. The longitudinal reinforcement (given in the Table for Reinforcement Dimensions) should be placed lengthwise, from top to bottom, 1 inch up from the under side of the slab. It is advisable to place rods of small diameter extending across the width of the slab, 12 to 24 inches apart, and these rods

should be securely wired to the larger rods at the intersections. Of course when steps have sides as in the right-hand view in Fig. 39, they add some support but it is wise to run a longitudinal rod the length of them, an inch or two from the top. See Table for Reinforcement Dimensions. Notice that the foot of the steps goes down into the earth about 18 inches to help anchor it firmly.

Self-supporting steps should have a firm support at the head, and Fig. 40 shows how a notch can be cut in

Reinforcement for Concrete Step Slabs

Slab dimensions		Round reinforcing rods			
		Longitudinal		Transverse	
Length	Thickness	Diameter	Spacing	Diameter	Spacing
Feet	Inches	Inch	Inches	Inch	Inches
2 to 3	4	$\frac{1}{4}$	10	$\frac{1}{4}$	12–18
3 to 4	4	$\frac{1}{4}$	$5\frac{1}{2}$	$\frac{1}{4}$	12–18
4 to 5	5	$\frac{1}{4}$	$4\frac{1}{2}$	$\frac{1}{4}$	18–24
5 to 6	5	$\frac{3}{8}$	7	$\frac{1}{4}$	18–24
6 to 7	6	$\frac{3}{8}$	6	$\frac{1}{4}$	18–24
7 to 8	6	$\frac{3}{8}$	4	$\frac{1}{4}$	18–24
8 to 9	7	$\frac{1}{2}$	7	$\frac{1}{4}$	18–24

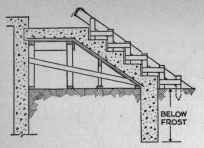

Fig. 40. Forms for self-supporting steps.

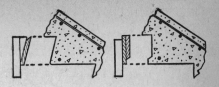

Fig. 41. Types of risers, with forms.

a masonry wall or the support of a concrete porch, and the head of the steps anchored to it.

The concrete should be mixed in the proportions of 1:2½:3½, unless a ¾-inch top course of mortar is to be applied, in which case a 1:3:5 mixture is satisfactory for supported slabs. The entire slab should be poured at one time, and the concrete should be mixed fairly dry so that when placed it will not be forced over the riser forms at the bottom of the steps by the pressure from above. The surface of the treads should be finished as soon as the base concrete is placed. A rough sand finish is preferable for a good foothold.

The riser should bear a certain relation to the width of the tread, and at the same time should be between 6 and 8 inches in height. Low risers and broad treads are generally preferable for outside steps. Risers 6½ to 7½ inches high, with properly proportioned treads, permit ascent with the least effort and are commonly used. High risers and narrow treads are used only where the horizontal distance is limited. A rather satisfactory formula is that twice the height of the riser, plus the width of the tread, should equal 25 inches. Thus two risers of 7½ inches total 15 inches and would leave a tread of 10 inches. Although not necessary, it is a good plan to project the tread ½ inch or ¾ inch beyond the riser. This may be accomplished in the manner shown in Fig. 41. Also the treads should have a pitch toward the front of from 1/32 to 1/16th of an inch in order to shed water.

CHAPTER 4

WATER AND DAMPNESS

The importance of analyzing first and acting second cannot be emphasized too strongly when considering problems caused by water and dampness around the home. When water appears on the side of walls in the basement, or discoloration takes place on a ceiling over the living room (Fig. 1), there is a tremendous impulse to immediately apply some remedy at the place where the water or damage appears. Too often, however, this does not solve the problem at all and only adds frustration to the general discomfort caused by the leakage. Sometimes, you need only apply a waterproofing compound to a wall or ceiling where trouble has arisen to correct the situation completely. But all too often homeowners who pursue this procedure blindly, find that the leakage has not been cured. At best, all they get is temporary relief. They blame the waterproofing product or the repair man, or both. Especially if outlandish claims were made for the waterproofing product. Usually, however, it is not the fault of the waterproofing method or the repair man. Reliable manufacturers do not claim their products are "cure-alls."

Whenever stains, dampness or any other problems caused by water are discovered, the first and most important thing to do is to find out the source of the difficulty. There may be no need for a waterproofing job on a wall which shows dampness if gutters and leaders on the roof are found to be clogged. Once this drainage problem has been repaired the dampness or leak may disappear. Dampness in a basement may not require laying a new floor if inspection reveals that the water has been permitted to accumulate around the foundation wall and thereby exercised extra pressure on the floor. Compact filling, in and around the foundation, and grading the soil away from the wall may be all that is needed to correct the problem.

SOURCES OF WATER

Rain

All houses are built to withstand a certain amount of rain, but excessive amounts will be a large factor in whether or not a home remains dry and free from leakage. When there is a large enough opening to permit rain water to enter the house directly, the obvious solution of course is to plug up the hole. Unfortunately, however, most problems caused by rain entering the home are not that simple. This is because the place or places where the rain water gets through are often difficult

Fig. I. Whenever water stains appear on a ceiling or on the side of walls in the basement, the first and most important thing to do is to find out the source of the trouble.

to find. The leakage and dampness are obvious enough, but the mystery is, where does the water come from.

Rain water frequently causes trouble when it seeps into cracks and crevices in the outside walls, roof or foundation and penetrates through to interior surfaces. These cracks and crevices may be caused by natural deterioration, poor materials or faulty workmanship. Ordinary rain may not penetrate these openings, but when the wind velocity and intensity is great, the force of the rain may cause considerable damage. A powerful wind-swept rain is certain to find weak spots in the masonry if they exist, and, if the rainfall lasts for any appreciable period, the danger of penetration becomes even greater. Intermittent rainfall is not nearly so damaging because the in-between periods give time for the drainage system to operate and the walls to dry out a bit. A steady

downpour may overtax the drainage system, however, and saturate the exterior surfaces so that interior dampness will result. The direction in which the rain is blowing is also very important. In most localities the wind driving the rains comes from a fixed direction. Occasionally, however, a freak storm occurs which drives the rain from an unusual direction and causes it to penetrate through openings which had always existed but hitherto had gone unnoticed because of the absence of rain from that direction. If you are going to buy an old house, therefore, do not depend entirely on stains on the walls to point out a possible water problem, because openings may exist on walls exposed to such freak storms. Even if the previous owner or real estate agent assures you that the rain always comes from one direction, check non-exposed walls carefully, too, and if they have cracks and weak points be sure they are repaired before you buy.

Today, many summer homes are being converted to year-round use. If your summer home has been customarily boarded up or enclosed with storm shutters during bad weather some weak spots may normally have been protected from heavy winter storms. It may, therefore, be necessary to make the glazing watertight for 12-month use and re-putty exposed points (Fig. 2).

Snow and Ice

Most of what has already been said about rain applies equally to snow and ice. In addition, however, there are important other considerations. When snow and ice melt they often form more water than would accumulate by rain during the same interval of time. This puts a greater burden on the drainage system. Leaks in weak spots in foundation walls or masonry will result when the water is not drained off fast enough. Ice can be especially troublesome if it clogs gutters and leaders, or other parts of the drainage system. Normally it should be allowed to melt of its own accord, unless there is an especially long period of freezing weather and chance that the weight of the ice, or its position on the roof may cause serious damage. When snow and ice on the roof is exposed to the warm rays of the sun during a winter thaw sometimes they are not able to run off properly to leaders and gutters because the latter were not similarly exposed to the sun, and are therefore still full of ice and snow. In such cases melted snow and ice may overflow the gutters on the roof and run down the outside of the wall, with the resulting water finding its way

Fig. 2. A summer home converted to year-round use will require treatment to make it waterproof. Re-putty exposed points that have customarily been protected by boards or enclosed with storm windows.

inside the house through some opening in a mortar joint or through faulty caulking at the top of the windows or under the window sill. If such a possibility exists use a bucket of hot water and soaked burlap rags to hasten the melting of the ice and snow in the leaders. Large icicle-like pieces, or chunks of ice which form and hang from the roof should never be yanked or hammered off, (Fig. 3). They may be stuck so securely that removal in such a manner will result in injury to the gutters or roofing material. If they must be taken off quickly, use steaming hot water or, to hasten melting, sprinkle with salt. Snow should not be allowed to stand too long around foundation walls or on top of roofs because the pressure may weaken masonry and roofing. Be sure that gutters and leaders are kept free of ice when the snow begins to melt. It's a good idea, too, to clear snow away from stairways, windows and other accesses to cellars as quickly as possible so that the water caused by melting will not have a chance to penetrate and cause damage.

Groundwater

There is a certain amount of water beneath the surface of the soil (Fig. 4), which is an important factor in waterproofing and dampproofing problems. This water may be underground streams which are sometimes present beneath the surface.

Or it may be water which, usually because of improper drain-

Fig. 3. Icicles which hang from a roof should never be yanked off. Their removal in this manner may result in damage to gutters and roofing material. Instead, use steaming hot water or sprinkle with salt.

age, accumulates on the surface outside a foundation wall, runs down into the excavation and gathers or seeps into the surface beneath the floor of the foundation. It may be rain, melted snow, ice, or even water from a defective or open fire hydrant, sprinkler system or garden hose, or any other source of outdoor water supply. If this groundwater gets too close to the bottom surface of the foundation the moisture will rise through capillary action and damp patches will appear on interior basement walls, especially after a heavy rain or snow fall. When the groundwater becomes so plentiful that it rises above the level of the basement floor it will cause standing water in the cellar and, at times, ex-

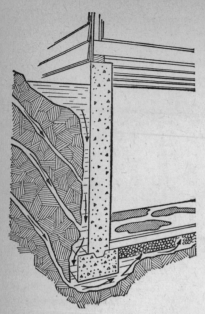

Fig. 4. Groundwater is an important factor in waterproofing problems. It stems either from underground streams or an accumulation on the surface outside a foundation wall.

openings in the foundation and cause dampness in the basement. This tendency of water to rise in much the same manner that oil rises in a lamp wick, or ink is pulled upwards by a piece of blotting paper is called "capillary action." The moisture from the wet soil, under and around the structure, is constantly seeking to climb higher and is often able to rise as much as 5 to 8 feet in very fine sands, silts, loams and clays. It will be less of a factor, however, in coarse sands where the extent of its rise may not exceed 2 or 3 feet.

Practically all masonry building materials and cement or lime mortars are porous. They will absorb moisture, therefore, in varying degrees. When the rate of evaporation inside the house is low, "capillary action" will cause the moisture from the wet ground to rise and enter the structural pores and cause seepage. When a basement is heated by dry heat and there is no leakage through cracks and other openings, frequent appearance of damp patches (Fig. 5), indicates that capillarity is taking place.

Where dampness occurs because of capillary action the thickness of the floor does not usually have to be increased if it is at least 4 inches thick. The most effective and lasting repairs are those made to the earth side of the basement wall. This requires a trench dug wide enough to work in and extending down to the bottom of the footing. (For full details on this method, see Chapter 8, "Is the Basement Dry?")

cessive dampness in the rooms above. It will also exert a heavy pressure on the floor and walls of the foundation and may cause cracks or separations. In such cases exterior surfaces must be waterproofed and strengthened unless drainage will relieve the force of the groundwater.

Capillary Action

If an underground stream runs beneath the surface of the soil, or groundwater saturates the earth below the bottom of the foundation, moisture may rise through the open pores in the soil, find tiny holes or

Test for Seepage

One method of checking to determine if there is leakage due to pressure, or seepage as a result of capillary action, is to make a simple test with calcium chloride, (Fig. 6). Place a glass dish against the basement wall high up above the damp area. Use tape or some other temporary means of holding the dish and seal the edge with a plastic caulking compound. Put a small quantity of calcium chloride inside the dish. Next put up a similar dish in the center of the damp area. If water collects in the lower dish (in the center of damp area) faster than in the upper one, it means that seepage is occurring. If neither dish collects water, seepage can be eliminated as the cause of damage.

WATER SUPPLY

Since most modern homes get their water piped in from some out-

Fig. 5. When a basement is heated by dry heat, and there is no leakage through cracks and other openings, frequent appearance of damp patches indicates that capillarity is taking place.

side source, there is a chance for this water to cause trouble when leaks develop in faucets or other connectors. This is usually an obvious deficiency except where pipes are hidden. When water or dampness appears in a partition wall it may be necessary to break through the wall in order to find the leak before proceeding to waterproof a wall or floor. Frequently the trouble can be located by following the exposed course of the pipes in the basement before they rise through the partitions. A shut-off valve, in the basement, will completely stop the flow of water. You can then find out which system of piping has sprung a leak. Turn on the faucet to empty the water from that pipe. Then try to listen for the sound of drops. Allow sufficient time to elapse, then turn on the water again and see if the leakage occurs as before. If the water supply is necessary before a plumber can be called, a leaky pipe can sometimes be temporarily fixed. Use a nail punch and hammer, and spread the metal around the leak so that it will cover it. This will work well with lead pipe because the metal is extremely soft. It is important to remember, however, that while some pipes are made of soft metal, such as lead and some forms of brass, these are not very brittle. Other pipes are made of hard metals, such as ordinary iron pipe and galvanized pipe, and are extremely brittle. Considerable damage may occur if brittle pipes are struck with a hammer or heavy hard tool, or if attempts are made to force metal from the pipe into an opening where a leak has developed.

Temporary repairs on the pipes can also often be made by forcing some plastic material into the opening where the leak occurs, and wrapping the pipe with some sturdy fabric such as ordinary tire tape, (Fig. 7). In the case of galvanized or brass pipe, another way is to take a piece of garden hose and split it on one side so that it can be fitted over the pipe where the leak has occurred. Hold the piece of garden hose securely in place and wrap a piece of wire around each end of it to make sure that it stays on tight. This method can also be used if there is more than one leak and will usually suffice until a new section can be installed. If leakage or water stains persist even after the plumbing has been repaired you can eliminate the water supply as a cause and look elsewhere for the source of the trouble.

Condensation, which will be discussed more fully in the next chapter, may form on cold water pipes in hot humid weather and also cause leakage or dampness, particularly in the basement. The use of any standard form of pipe covering for insulation will prevent this condition.

Pipe Openings

Since the outside rain is constantly looking for holes or cracks through which it may penetrate the house, breaks in the foundation or exterior walls where water pipes are brought into the home are often weak spots where outside water seeps through. The foundation and masonry may be

Fig. 6. Test for seepage—if water collects in lower dish of calcium chloride faster than in the upper one, seepage is taking place; if neither dish collects water, seepage can be eliminated as the cause of the damage

effectively waterproofed, but sometimes space around openings where pipes enter, is not properly sealed and water creeps through tiny holes or cracks. Examine these places carefully to see if there is evidence of seepage or dampness. Such gaps can be plugged with a small amount of caulking compound forced into the opening with a putty knife or similar small tool. A small screwdriver in place of a putty knife can also be used.

Spilling

When the bathtub or sink overflows water will either form a large puddle on the bathroom or kitchen floor, or it will seek openings in the floor and seep into the walls or ceilings below. If the flooring is com-

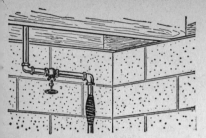

Fig. 7. A temporary repair on a pipe can be made by forcing some plastic material into the opening where the leak occurs, and wrapping the pipe with a sturdy fabric such as ordinary tire tape.

pletely waterproofed the water will merely remain on the surface on which it spills. The chief problem then is to mop it up or pump it out. But if it should flow through cracks and drip down on the surfaces below it may cause serious damage to wall decorations or furniture. Usually this condition will disappear after a few days of dry weather and, unless actual stains have resulted, the water on the wall will dry up and no longer be noticeable. Where washing machines or dish washing machines are likely to cause a certain amount of spilling each time they are used, the machines should be set up where the spilling is not objectionable. If this is not practical some means of draining off the excess water must be found, or the machine should be set up on top of a drainage pan.

Humidity

Another important source of water is the moisture in air. During cold weather months it is highly desirable to have proper amounts of moisture in the air inside the house. Doctors say it is beneficial from a health standpoint and it also helps prevent the joints in furniture and woodwork from drying out. In addition, too much dry air in the house during the winter will make it necessary to use more heat to make people comfortable. In hot weather months, however, it is generally cooler and more comfortable indoors when the humidity is low. The expression, "It's not the heat, it's the humidity" is often heard during sticky summer weather. In both cold and hot weather, moreover, there is always a certain amount of humidity in the air.

Humidity is simply a term used to describe moisture in the air. It is an invisible water vapor or gas. When the temperature increases the air is able to hold more water vapor and the humidity is high, (Fig. 8). When the air contains the amount of water vapor that it can hold at a specific temperature, the humidity of that air is 100 per cent.

Too much humidity in the home causes condensation and may lead to dampness and other water problems. Insufficient humidity may cause damage to furniture or woodwork. Both extremes cause discomfort, are unhealthy, and should be checked. Humidity can be measured with the aid of one of two instruments, the psychrometer and hygrometer. Both are obtainable from dealers in scientific equipment.

Too much moisture, or high humidity in the home can best be corrected by means of proper ventilation. Often opening windows and doors for short periods of time will be all that is needed to lower the humidity. This is especially true in the winter. In the summer ventilating fans or air-conditioning may be required. Additional moisture in the air during the winter can often be obtained by keeping the water pan provided with the warm air furnace filled with water. The air coming up through the registers is then likely to have additional water vapor added to it. Special water pans may also be attached to radiators or placed on top of electric heaters. In addition, there are a number of efficient humidifiers on the market which will control the moisture content of the air at the desired level. The problem is not generally acute, however, from a waterproofing standpoint, unless the humidity becomes condensa-

tion. *Condensation is discussed in Chapter 5.*

HYDROSTATIC PRESSURE

Wherever water is confined in any manner, pressure is exerted on all sides and on the bottom of the vessel or opening in which the water stands. The amount of pressure varies with the depth of the water. It is not affected by the volume. For example, 2 feet of water in a ten gallon tank would exert the same amount of pressure as 2 feet of water in a twenty gallon tank, (Fig. 9). In the case of a home, the space in the ground dug out, or excavated in order to lay a foundation, serves as a receptacle or container for water. It may be filled more or less with rain water or water which seeps in through the ground. In a similar fashion the foundation itself is also

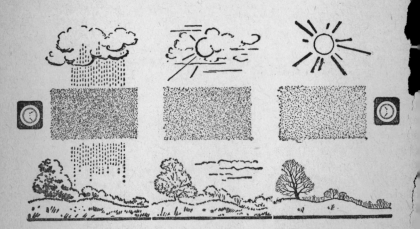

Fig. 8. Humidity is a term to describe moisture in the air. As the temperature increases the air is able to hold more water vapor and the humidity is high. Conversely, as the temperature decreases, humidity decreases.

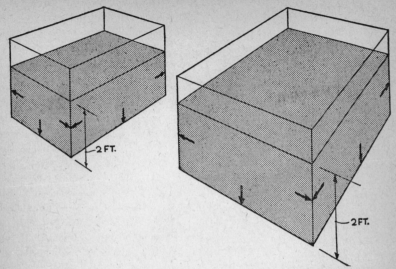

Fig. 9. Hydrostatic pressure varies with the depth of the water. It is not affected by the volume. As illustrated above, 2 feet of water in a 10-gallon tank exerts the same amount of pressure as 2 feet of water exerts in a 20-gallon tank.

potential water vessel and may receive water the same way.

As this water rises in the ground nd gathers below the bottom of the oundation and up around foundaon walls, it exerts a certain force gainst these surfaces which is called Hydrostatic Pressure." The amount f this pressure depends entirely on e height of the water rising above the basement floor. It doesn't make any difference if the area is 100 square feet or 1,000 square feet, (Fig. 10). The vertical dimension is the controlling factor. The amount of pressure is entirely independent of the amount or volume of water. Hydrostatic pressure is measured in pounds per square inch, or in pounds per square foot. A static head of water will exert a pressure

of 62½ pounds per square foot for each foot of height of the water. Sometimes during construction work water pressure must be relieved by pumping until the concret have been placed and have eloped its designed strength.

Frequently, hydrostatic pressure can be remedied by improved drainage. If ground conditions do not permit natural drainage, artificial means (Fig. 11), must be developed to allow the water to run off before it is able to build up enough pressure to destroy the basement floor slab. When proper drainage cannot be provided, it is necessary to install a new floor strong enough to withstand the maximum water pressure, or to drain the water off to a sump pit where it can be pumped away or run off at a higher level. Hydro-static pressure also takes place on the roof. This occurs when drains on roofs are clogged up from flying paper or dry leaves and water cannot run out through the drain. It will then accumulate on the roof and create a hydrostatic pressure. This water may tend to rise above the height of flashings and seep over the top and in between the flashing and the parapet wall. It may then find its way down through the brick work and cause stains on the inside of the walls below. Proper inspection of the drainage system on the roof will help prevent this from happening. Trou-

ble can also be avoided by applying a black dampproofing paint with an asphalt or tar base from the top of the flashing to the coping on top of the parapet wall.

WHAT IS WATERPROOFING?

The methods and materials (Fig. 12), used to prevent the penetration of water through walls and floors when such walls and floors are subjected to hydrostatic pressure are known as waterproofing. The term is frequently and incorrectly applied also to ways and means of prevent-

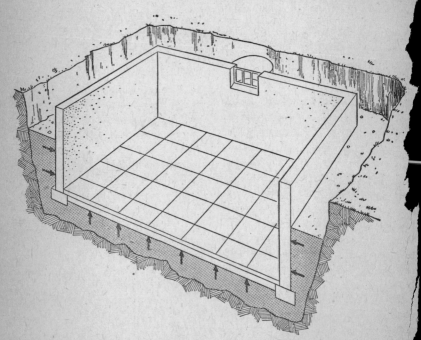

Fig. 10. Hydrostatic pressure depends entirely upon the height of the water rising above the basement floor. Regardless of whether the area is 100 or 1,000 square feet—the vertical dimension is the controlling factor.

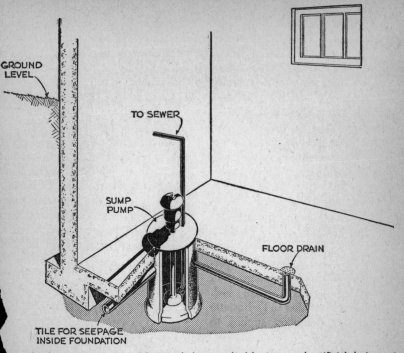

GROUND LEVEL

TO SEWER

SUMP PUMP

FLOOR DRAIN

TILE FOR SEEPAGE INSIDE FOUNDATION

Fig. 11. Hydrostatic pressure can frequently be remedied by improved artificial drainage to allow the water to run off before it is able to build up enough pressure to destroy the basement floor slab.

ing and correcting water problems due to condensation and seepage. In the main, waterproofing is used where water pressure, of hydrostatic nature, is involved. This occurs below the ground level or on the roof. Waterproofing is also used, however, to prevent damage due to the action of running water, such as in shower baths.

In foundations, waterproofing is used to keep water from causing dampness or actually leaking into the basement. It is also used to protect the concrete. Its purpose on the roof and on basement floors is to

keep the water out, while its use in connection with shower baths is to protect the floor and walls and prevent water from escaping into other parts of the house. On retaining walls it is used to prevent disintegration of the structure. On floor and foundation joints it not only excludes water, but it also acts as a seal against termites.

For many, waterproofing is a completely baffling subject which appears to be a matter of chance or luck. This feeling exists because of the bitter experiences of some homeowners who compare their unhappy fate, when they get leakage, with neighbors and friends whose homes have no water problems at all. This is especially true of homeowners in a development where every house is alike in structure, was built the same way and at approximately the same time. Yet one has a water problem, while the house next door, or indirectly in back, does not. The answer will be found in tracking down the source of the problem.

Dampproofing

This term is often used interchangeably with waterproofing. It is intended, however, to include only methods and materials used to prevent moisture and dampness from penetrating the home when such conditions are not due to hydrostatic pressure. Dampproofing applied to

Fig. 12. Waterproofing compound being dumped into portland cement mixture.

a surface is supposed to make the material impermeable to water when it is present in relatively small quantities every now and then. While waterproofing is also naturally and inherently dampproofing, dampproofing cannot be waterproofing.

Dampproofing generally consists of a water-repellent surface coating applied by brush, spray (Fig. 13), or trowel. A good one will penetrate into, and fill the pores of a surface, is sufficiently elastic to conform to expansion and contraction, and is insoluble in and unaffected by acids or alkalis that may come in contact with it either in the water it is intended to repel, or on the surfaces to which it is applied.

EFFECT OF DAMPNESS AN WATER LEAKAGE

Whether you are about to pu chase a new home, or you are inter ested in maintaining the home tha you have, you must certainly recog nize the tremendous importance eliminating or minimizing dampnes and water leakage.

Health

A damp house will increase the susceptibility to all types of sickness and diseases. Dampness represents, therefore, not only discomfort but also a possible cause of a major health problem.

Appearance

Water stains on any surface will mar the looks of a room, (Fig. 14). Wall paper that is blistered or peel-

Fig. 13. Dampproofing being applied with a spray on an outside wall.

ng and other surfaces that are dis-olored detract immensely from the tractiveness of the home and will nder an expensive interior decorat-ng job completely valueless. Since othing stains or causes the amount of damage to the appearance of the home as much as water does, the importance of eliminating this haz-ard becomes quite evident.

On the upper floors, watch par-ticularly for stains under the window sills (Fig. 15), or at the intersections of walls and ceilings. In the attic, look for stains under the roof beams or on the attic floor where water may have come through the roof.

Life of House

Water has a deteriorating effect on lumber and other materials. Leaks will cause rotting and gradual disintegration which will reduce the life of the house and make it age much faster. On the other hand, if the house is maintained properly and kept free of water problems its life can be lengthened considerably. It can be expanded and remodeled in keeping with modern trends and will give longer and much more satisfactory service than many newer constructions. Moreover, freedom from leakage will add considerably to the value of a house, old or new.

LOCATION OF THE HOUSE

In looking for the source of a possible water problem be sure to take the location of your house into consideration. Many factors about the actual place where a home is situated are in themselves causes for damp basements or leaky walls.

General Climatic Conditions

If the house is situated in a region where there is frequent rainfall the need for proper waterproofing and dampproofing is more acute than if the home were in a dry or arid location. On the other hand, humidity that might be lacking in one area, can cause a greater condensation problem in a home situated in a region noted for high humidity. Homes built near the seacoast have different problems from those situated farther inland, not only from the standpoint of rainfall perhaps, but also because in a seacoast area the outside masonry will be subjected to more salt in the air

Fig. 14. Water stains on any surface will mar the looks of a room and render an expensive interior decorating job completely valueless.

Fig. 15. On upper floors watch particularly for water stains under the window sills.

and this may have a deteriorating affect.

Site

Houses situated in valleys may have basements that are below the groundwater level, while homes that are built on flat ground may have drainage problems which should be looked into. If the house is near a water stream it is quite likely to have a greater waterproofing problem than one which is well removed from any open body of water.

Nearby Homes

It is not only important to find out where the water from your own house is going to be drained off, with certainty that you can keep it away from your foundation, but it is also a good idea to check on the drainage system used by neighboring houses, (Fig. 16). If you discover that they are draining off water onto

your property this may be the cause of water in your basement.

Nature of Soil

The soil and sub-soil have a great deal to do with the dryness of the house. They should be open and porous so that water is admitted readily, as in the case of sands, gravels and loams. A very marshy soil should be avoided because it is obviously already saturated with water.

Trees and Shrubbery

These should be examined to see how they are affecting the drainage system and also whether or not they are causing too much shade and consequent dampness, (Fig. 17). Trees may be directing too much water onto a particular part of the roof or masonry, thereby causing un-

Fig. 16. Equally as important as finding out where the water from your house is going to be drained off, is to check on the drainage system used by neighboring houses.

Fig. 17. Trees and shubbery should be examined carefully to note whether they are causing too much shade and consequent dampness.

even pressure which may weaken this one segment.

OLD AND NEW HOUSES

While much has been learned about waterproofing, and practically all new homes are built with this factor in mind, there is so much haste in building today, and such a tremendous desire to cut corners and keep costs down, that many of the newer homes have more waterproofing problems than older ones. This fact is almost entirely due to cost, haste and negligence. So much has been learned about waterproofing today that there is really no reason why a new house should not be as completely free from this problem as possible. It is therefore necessary to be extremely cautious when buying or building a new house to make sure that proper waterproofing has

been taken into consideration. It is certainly much more economical in the long run to spend a few dollars more on better materials and proper waterproofing than to save that expense and have costlier problems later on.

Remodeling old Homes

Where an old home has been without trouble from water leakage in the past, this problem should be carefully considered when attempting any remodeling. This is especially true when converting the heating system from coal to oil or gas. The result often is a water condition in the basement where one did not exist previously. This may have been due to improper insulation between the oil flame and the basement floor under the oil flame. It will cause cracks or even burnt concrete through which water can seep into the basement.

CHAPTER 5

CONDENSATION

When there is a temperature change in the air the humidity or water vapor in the air is also affected. If the temperature rises, the humidity increases; if the temperature drops, the humidity drops accordingly. Now, if a mass of warm air in a room comes in contact with a colder object, for example, the effect at the point where the contact is made will be to cause the warm air to throw off some of its humidity or water vapor. Condensation takes place and liquid or droplets of water are formed. This is exactly what happens when the warm air in the basement during the summer comes in contact with cold pipes or walls and causes dripping, puddles, or water stains.

Another example of condensation is seen in window panes which become "cloudy" or "sweaty" when the weather is cold outside and warm indoors. It is especially important today because many of the newer homes with thermal insulation, weather stripping, and storm windows are built so "tight" that moisture in the warm air inside has no way of joining the cold air outdoors. The result is that it then condenses on cooler, interior surfaces. You then find paint peeling and wood deteriorating. Water deposits drip on floors

and other surfaces causing dampness and discoloration. Older homes, especially frame houses, are often more porous, on the other hand, and thus enable the warm, humid air inside to mix more freely with the outside air, (Fig. 1). This would appear to be critical of the newer dwellings which are built to conserve heat through greater insulation, but such is not the case. Condensation can be controlled in all homes.

Causes of Condensation

Extensive use of appliances which give off water vapor such as washing machines and various cooking appliances cause condensation. It also occurs in many of the newer homes today where low-cost designs turn up small rooms and low ceilings. The amount of space in which the air can circulate is important. Water vapor in a small area will condense more rapidly. Plants, animals, and people also contribute to the amount of water vapor in a home. So does vapor from showers, baths and indoor clothes-drying.

Many low-cost homes today which are being built without basements (Fig. 2), create problems due, again, to condensation. In this type of home an enclosed crawl space takes the place of the standard cellar. This

Fig. I. The frame type of house is often more porous allowing the warm humid air inside to mix more freely with the outside air.

area beneath the first floor often gets damp and, if there is no ventilation, the water vapor finds its way up into walls, attics, and living areas and condenses.

Outside the House

Exterior paint can be badly damaged by condensation. Free water or ice, which collects behind the siding may run over the surface of the siding when it condenses. It will frequently absorb extractives from the wood and cause stains. If it soaks the siding it may cause the paint to blister and peel. Where moist conditions are present for a considerable length of time, decay may occur.

Generally, the outside walls "breathe" enough to take off the moisture that does form. A masonry wall, for example, is quite porous and the water vapor that it collects will be thrown back out if it is blocked on the inside by a vapor barrier. In the case of wood sheathing and siding, as noted above, water vapor is often collected and condensation results. It is often advisable to construct small vents just under the cornice and above the footing, (Fig. 3). These should be protected from the weather by mouldings.

Snow and Ice Dams

Leakage of water into buildings is sometimes caused by ice dams and is often mistaken for condensation. Snow and ice dams are usually found after heavy snowfalls. If the temperature is a little below freezing, the heat from indoors will melt the ice and snow along the roof surface. Then the water creeps down over the surface, and when it reaches the overhang of the roof, freezes and builds up a ledge of solid ice. The rest of the ice and snow which is melting then has no place to go because of the barrier set up by the ice ledge. Consequently it backs under and between the shingles and enters the building.

To prevent such leakage the eaves must be protected. A single course of heavy roofing felt should be placed over the eaves, (Fig 4). Extend it upwards and well above the inside line of the wall. This will prevent ice and snow dams from forming in the eaves. Sheet metal can also be used as a lining material. Though this condition is often referred to as condensation, it is essentially a matter of drainage and insulation.

TESTS FOR WATER CONDITIONS

A water condition in the house is due to one of three things: seepage, leakage, or condensation. Unless the condition is obviously due to condensation, it will be useful to apply one of the following tests:

1. Take a small pocket mirror, or thin sheet of bright metal or glass, and glue or cement it to the portion of the floor or wall that frequently becomes damp. Use the smallest amount of adhesive that will give firm contact. Leave it up for a few hours so that it may assume the temperature of the wall. Then examine the surface of the mirror or other object. If no droplets of water form on the mirror, but the wall continues to be damp, the cause of the difficulty is not condensation. If droplets do appear, however, condensation has occurred. It may not, however, be the only cause of dampness in the surrounding areas.

Fig. 2. Homes with crawl spaces instead of basements are likely to have condensation owing to a lack of ventilation in the area beneath the first floor.

2. Place a thermometer in contact with the damp portion of the floor or wall and cover it with several layers of woolen cloth or blanket so that the temperature of the thermometer will approximate that of the masonry. By means of wet and dry bulb thermometers and psychrometric tables, (available from the Superintendent of Documents, Government Printing Office, Washington 25, D. C., for five cents), determine the temperature of the dew point of the air in the basement. If the temperature of the masonry is lower than the dew point of the air, condensation contributes to the dampness.

3. Make a plaster of Paris ring about three inches in diameter and attach it to the surface to be tested, (Fig. 5). Before the plaster sets, place the closed end of an ordinary drinking glass tightly on the surface of the plaster so that no air reaches the masonry surface under the glass. The ring should be at least one inch thick so that the glass is at least one inch away from the surface to be tested. After 24 hours elapse, examine the two faces. If the one surrounding the plaster is damp while the surface under the glass is dry, the dampness is caused by condensation. If moisture appears under the glass, water seepage is indicated.

4. Select a spot on a basement wall which is wet and chip off about one square inch of the surface with a chisel and hammer. Examine the color of the exposed surface and the wall where the piece has been chipped away. If water has been

Fig. 3. Vents place under the cornices and above the footing aid outside walls to "breathe" thereby offsetting condensation.

seeping through the wall this exposed surface will be dark and damp. If the presence of water was due, however, to condensation, the exposed surface will be light in color, dry, and dusty in appearance.

CORRECTIVE MEASURES

If we could remove the causes of condensation we might have a simple solution to the problem. Unfortunately it is not as easy as that. We cannot do without our many appli-

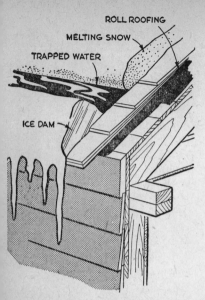

ROLL ROOFING

MELTING SNOW

TRAPPED WATER

ICE DAM

Fig. 4. Roof leakage is sometimes caused by ice dams. In such cases, the eaves should be protected by the use of heavy roofing felt.

ances and other comforts, and there is no reason why we should. It is more practical to contrive to maintain even temperatures and reduce marked differences at points where warm air strikes cold surfaces. Ventilation, therefore, and some form of vapor barrier or insulation, are the principal methods employed to control condensation.

Ventilation

Wherever possible, appliances which give off large quantities of water vapor, such as automatic clothes-dryers, should be equipped with some means of ventilation which can carry the vapor directly outdoors, (Fig. 6). Gas-operated hot water heaters and stoves often give off hydrogen which combines with the oxygen in the air to form water vapor and increases the humidity in the house. Care should be taken to keep vents working properly and, where vents or flues are absent, they should be installed.

CRAWL SPACE

In recent years there has been a tendency to cut costs by omitting basements in home construction. Instead, such dwellings usually have what is known as a crawl space. This is an enclosed area between the ground and the first floor. It may be only a foot or two, or it may be several feet high. The crawl space must, however, be suitable for the installation and maintenance of mechanical lines and equipment when they are placed below the first floor. Walls enclosing the area are usually made of masonry, wood siding, asbestos cement board, metal sheets, or other similar materials supported on light framing.

Soil around the crawl space must be graded away from the building to prevent water from entering into the area and wetting the inside earth (Fig. 7). In addition, drains in the crawl space itself are recommended if the floors are below the outside grade. When this has been properly attended to and moisture and dampness are still a serious problem in the living quarters above, condensation caused by excessive moisture in the crawl space is generally at fault.

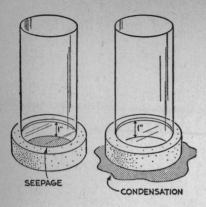

SEEPAGE

CONDENSATION

Fig. 5. You can easily apply this test to learn if dampness is caused by water seepage or condensation.

Control by Ventilation

Where there is no other means of controlling condensation, at least four ventilating openings should be installed. Place one near each corner of the building, (Fig. 8). Figure the total net amount of crawl space ventilation required on the basis of two square feet of ventilating space per 100 linear feet of building perimeter, plus one third of one per cent of the crawl space ground area. Openings should be placed as high up as possible in the walls of the crawl space. If this ventilation is the only means of controlling condensation, keep the vents open throughout the year. Also make sure the floors over the crawl space are properly insulated. Plumbing pipes should also be insulated and, if the building is situated on a sloping site, drain tiles on the sloping side are recommended to permit water to drain away from the crawl space.

Control by Ground Cover

In many northern areas where it is not practical to allow a completely free sweep of cold air below a dwelling floor, another method can be used. In this instance, condensation is reduced by stopping the moisture from the ground entering the air in the crawl space. The ground is covered with a vapor-resistant durable material like a good waterproof concrete slab or heavy roll roofing, (Fig. 9). The roll roofing, either mineral surfaced or plain, should be laid over a rough graded surface. At least two-inch lapped joints must be allowed, but generally they do not require any cementing material. The

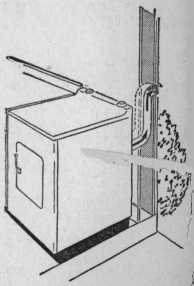

Fig. 6. Household appliances give off large amounts of water vapor. The illustration above reveals how a conduit directs damaging vapors outdoors.

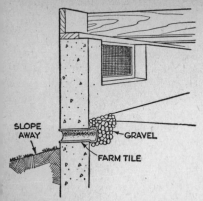

Fig. 7. The home with a crawl space must have the soil graded away from the building to avoid wetting the inside earth.

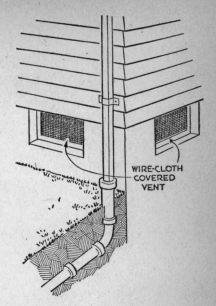

Fig. 8. A ventilator opening in each corner of the building will aid control of condensation in homes with crawl spaces.

roll roofing should weigh at least 55 pounds per 100 square feet. Some ventilation should also be provided, but it need be only 10 per cent of that required when ventilation is the only method used. Even if the soil is not completely smooth the roofing material will become soft and will conform to the contour of the soil within a short time. If there is a chance that water might get inside the foundation wall, be sure the soil surface below the building is kept above the outside grade. A soil cover will be especially valuable where the soil has high capillarity and the water table is continually near the surface.

Condensation control may also be obtained by spreading a four-inch layer of gravel over the soil in the crawl space. The gravel should be small in diameter so there will not be too much space between pieces, but should not be less than one-eighth inch in diameter.

VENTILATING THE ATTIC

In order to work effectively as a means of controlling condensation in the attic, the amount of ventilation must be adequate and should be properly located and operated continuously. For a gable, or modified hip roof, louver-type ventilators are recommended. Place them as high up as possible since warm air moves upward and out of the building. Use a mesh size which is not too small, but which will still keep out insects. Extremely fine wire cloth should be avoided because it restricts the movement of air and is easily clogged by dust and lint. In flat-roof structures, vents should be installed below the eave communicating with the space above the thermal insulation between the roof joists, (Fig 10). Make certain that airways above the insulation are clear from one side of the building to the other. Install vents as near the outside of the cornice as possible to minimize the amount of snow driven through the ventilators by the wind. A vapor barrier should also be used on the warm side of the ceiling.

Vapor Barriers

Condensation on walls, floors, ceilings and roofs may be remedied most effectively by means of a vapor barrier, used alone, or combined with ventilation. The barrier blocks the passage of water vapor. It is usually placed on the interior side of the insulation, thus preventing the cold, outside air from coming in contact with the warm inside surfaces where it might condense. Effective vapor barriers are: building papers that are saturated and coated with a high gloss asphalt; laminated or duplex uncreped kraft papers having an undamaged layer of asphalt between them and spread to a thickness of 60 pounds per ream; metal foils without folds or creases that have been mounted on materials, such as paper and composition board lath; sufficient coats of lead and oil paint, rubber base paint, asphalt, and certain types of aluminum paint which result in a smooth unbroken, glossy finish on the surface to which they are applied, and certain specialty wall coverings of thin material having special vapor-resistant coatings. The latter are often used in bathrooms and kitchens where the surface must be cleaned often.

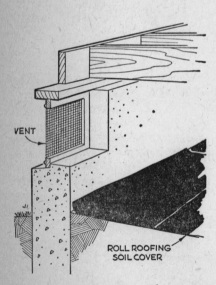

VENT

ROLL ROOFING
SOIL COVER

Fig. 9. A ground covering with a vapor-resistant durable material, or heavy roll roofing, is used in many northern areas where it is not practical to allow a completely free sweep of cold air below dwelling floors.

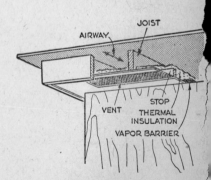

AIRWAY   JOIST

VENT   STOP
THERMAL
INSULATION
VAPOR BARRIER

Fig. 10. In flat-roof structures, vents are best placed below the eaves, joining with the space above the thermal insulation between the roof joists.

Two coats of aluminum paint applied under the decorative wall or ceiling finish will prove helpful as a vapor barrier when it is not practical to install sheet materials. Such coatings may be aluminum, asphalt, or oil paints, as well as some enamels. First remove the wallpaper, and then thoroughly clean and patch the plaster.

Before applying aluminum paint, give the plaster one coat of plaster primer or sealer, followed by two coats of aluminum paint. This will reduce penetration of vapor into the wall and the surface can then be covered with wallpaper or other interior finish. Asphalt should not be used on exposed walls, but if enough coats are applied to the back of plywood or similar inside finishes to give them a glossy surface, it will prove satisfactory as a barrier also. Oil paints, semi-gloss wall enamels, or gloss wall enamels may be used on plastered walls, provided the walls have been primed with two coats of wall primer.

In new construction, vapor barriers may be installed on the inner face of wall studs, or the bottom of top floor ceiling joists, before the inside finish is applied (Fig. 11). Barriers will be most effective if they are fitted to form a continuous, unbroken membrane and are installed on the warm, or room side of the insulation, which is usually behind the lath and plaster or other finish material.

Place sheet-form vapor barriers in the attic above existing top floor ceilings and cut them so they will fit

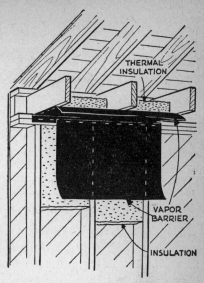

Fig. 11. In new construction, barriers against vapor may be installed on the inner face of wall studs, or the bottom of top floor ceiling joists, before the inside finish is applied.

between the joists. Then lay them on top of the ceiling. Loose-fill, batt, or blanket-type insulation may then be placed between the joists on top of the vapor barrier. Some batt or blanket-type insulation has a vapor barrier attached, in which case no additional barrier is necessary. Lay this type of insulation between the joists on the ceiling with the vapor barrier side down.

In an unfinished attic, install batt or blanket-type insulation between the exposed roof rafters, (Fig. 12). Tack it to the side of the rafters so as to leave one air space between the top of the insulation and bottom of the roof boards, and another air space between the bottom of the in-

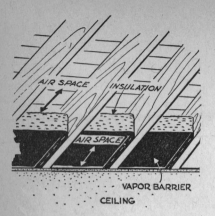

Fig. 12. The spaces between exposed roof rafters offer good places in unfinished attics for the installation of batt or blanket-type installation.

sulation and the bottom of the rafters. If the insulation has a vapor barrier attached, install it with the vapor barrier side down. If it does not have the vapor barrier attached, apply sheet-form vapor barrier material to the bottom edge of the rafters. When this has been done, apply ceiling finish.

If loose-fill insulation is used between the rafters of an unfinished attic, tack sheet-form barrier material to the lower edge of the rafters and apply ceiling finish before the insulation is blown in. If loose-fill insulation is to be blown between the rafters in a finished attic, no vapor barrier exists, paint the warm side or face the ceiling with at least two coats of aluminum paint before wallpaper or other decorative finish is applied.

Whenever insulation is placed between roof rafters, it is necessary to provide space between the bottom of the roof boards and the top of the insulating material. The space will serve as a good insulator if properly ventilated with outdoor air.

Around Outlets

Vapor barriers should be well fitted around electric switch and outlet boxes to prevent water vapor from getting through to the wall. Staple the paper to the wood structure and lay it over the outlet box. In this position it can be broken or cut by striking it above the edge of the box with a hammer. This will crush or break the paper. It can also be cut along the edge of the box with a sharp knife. Then push the barrier over the edge of the box. Be especially careful not to tear it. The flow of water vapor through the box itself cannot be completely eliminated. No more openings should be made, however, by the electrician than are absolutely necessary. Blanket insulation with a vapor barrier attached should be cut diagonally over the box. Remove most of the fiber between the covers and tuck the corners down at the sides of the box.

Condensation on Pipes

Cold water pipes in the basement can be prevented from causing condensation in hot, humid weather if they are covered. A cylindrical-shaped, split pipe covering of wood insulating felt with a canvas jacket is one type of insulation which may be used for this purpose. It comes in 3-foot length of various thicknesses and is made for standard pipe sizes.

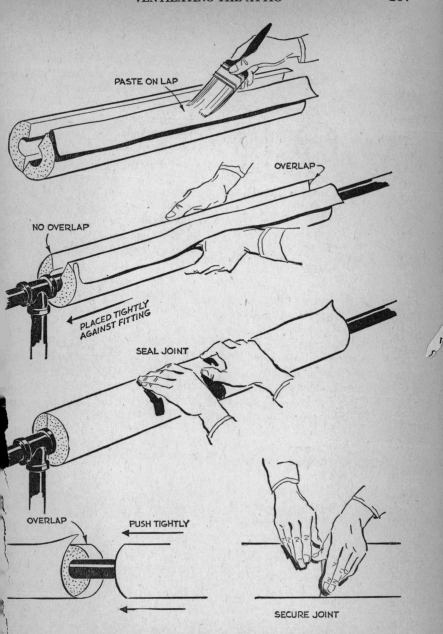

PASTE ON LAP

OVERLAP

NO OVERLAP

PLACED TIGHTLY AGAINST FITTING

SEAL JOINT

OVERLAP

PUSH TIGHTLY

SECURE JOINT

Fig. 13. The tendency for cold water pipes to drip during humid weather can be prevented by the use of a wood insulating felt with a canvas jacket.

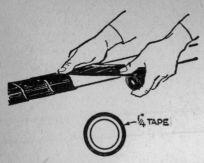

Fig. 14. Tape insulation may be wrapped around cold-water pipes to a thickness of about ¼ inch.

Pipes should be in good condition and cleaned. Loosen the canvas lap on the pipe covering and brush along the edge with paste to refasten the lap. Encase the pipe with a section of covering placed with the open side up (Fig. 13), and with the end which has no canvas-joint overlap, placed tight against the fitting and pressed closely together. Paste the lap securely over the longitudinal joint. Apply the second section in the same manner and push tightly against the first. Then seal the joint between the two sections by pasting the overlap attached to the first section over the joint. Continue covering the pipe in this way until the next fitting is reached. When a short section is needed, cut the covering with a sharp knife or handsaw.

Apply the first coat of asbestos cement on the fittings by applying a half-inch second coat, or one of the same thickness as the pipe covering. This coat should be trowelled smooth and bevelled down to meet the surface of the pipe covering. The asbestos cement on the fittings is then protected by a canvas jacket, which should be the same weight as that used on the pipe covering. It should be pasted down smoothly and a vapor-resistant covering applied to the surface to prevent water vapor from reaching the surface of the metal pipe.

To improve the appearance, apply two coats of spar-varnish aluminum paint to the canvas jacket followed by one or two coats of paint in any desired color. Aluminum foil, such as is sold for kitchen use, may be wrapped around the jacket instead of using aluminum paint. It is wise to use a paint which contains a fungicide to prevent mildew if the basement is inclined to be damp. If appearance is not an important consideration, the canvas jacket may be wrapped and sealed with aluminum foil or with asphalt-impregnated paper, or it may be painted with an unbroken coating of asphalt.

Tape-form insulating coverings are also available which may be wrapped spirally around cold-water pipes to a thickness of about one-fourth inch (Fig. 14), and thick paints mixed with insulating materials may be applied to pipes in a coating of about one-fourth inch thickness.

INSULATING OLD WALLS

Cold walls will often "sweat" or show damp spots when warm water vapor in the room strikes them. This is caused by condensation and can be a serious source of trouble. The walls should be treated and made warmer by applying furring strips. These are nailed over the old plaster. New lath and plaster, insulating board, or insulating material and wall board are then applied. Remove the trim before applying the new surface. When the wall is finished, insert pieces of wood behind the trim before it is replaced to bring it forward to form a suitable offset. You can also leave the old trim in place and apply new trim on top of it after plastering.

Brick Walls

Brick walls which have been furred on the inside may be satisfactory without further insulation unless the climate is severe. If more insulation is desired, however, the inside finish should be removed and blanket or other type of insulation may be placed between the furring strips.

Lath, composed of either gypsum board or fiberboard with or without aluminum foil on the back, may be used as a plaster base. Where a foil-backed board is used, a reflective air space is formed which has two or three times the insulating value of an ordinary air space, or about that of two-thirds of an inch of blanket insulation. Different types of wall-board, with or without metal foil on the back, may be used instead of lath and plaster.

Storm Windows

During the winter, window panes often become frosty. When the frost melts it runs down the pane, spills onto the sill and floor and can cause considerable damage. If this condition cannot be corrected by reducing the amount of water vapor in the house, the installation of storm windows will help keep the cold air away from the panes and the possibility of condensation will be reduced. Unless the storm windows are also needed to help retain heat in the house, they do not have to be put up for all window openings. They should be provided only for the windows on the side of the house facing prevailing winds.

Attic Insulation

The roof is the most exposed part of the house. It is subject to strong cold winds in winter and to direct rays of sun in summer, (Fig. 15). If an attic is uninsulated a great deal of heat may be lost through the roof during winter months. One evidence of this is very rapid melting of snow on the roof. In the summer, an attic that is hotter than other parts of the house indicates poor insulation, too.

If the attic is not being used for living quarters and it is unnecessary to keep the temperature in that space at a comfortable level, insulation in the form of batts, blankets, or loose-fill material should be laid between the floor joists of the attic, on top of the ceiling below. If the attic is not floored, lay boards across the floor joists so you can walk on them while you are laying the insulation. When the attic is being occupied and you wish to keep the temperature there comfortable throughout the year, apply insulation to the underside of the roof between the rafters, and to the end walls. If there is a metal or asphaltic roofing, which offers resistance to escaping water vapor, place a good vapor barrier on the underside of the rafters.

HEAT PENETRATES

HEAT ESCAPES

Fig. 15. The importance of roof insulation cannot be overemphasized, as it is the most exposed part of the house. Winter winds lash it and the summer sun scorches it.

Roof insulation should be installed so that there is a space of two to three inches between it and the undersides of the roof boards. Sufficient ventilation of this space should also be provided. This can be done by leaving small openings or cracks at the eaves, or by installing louvers (Fig. 16)), in the end walls which communicate with the triangular space between the roof and a false ceiling over the attic. Vapor barriers and ventilation between insulation and roof will prevent condensation of moisture in winter which could wet and damage the roof structure and cause dampness below.

If the attic is to be completely equipped for occupancy, the enclosing walls and ceiling should be insulated and vapor barriers installed. Then a finish surface material may be applied.

Basement Walls

Detection of condensation in the basement is more important than in any other part of the house. Basement walls are frequently subjected to contact with outside water and often to water under hydrostatic pressure. The appearance of water on the surface of the basement wall will naturally raise the suspicion that water leaks and is penetrating from the outside to the inside. If this is the case the wall will probably need to be waterproofed. If, on the other hand, the presence of a wet surface on the inside is due to condensation of warm humid air on a cold foundation wall, this cannot be cured with waterproofing. Instead, the conden-

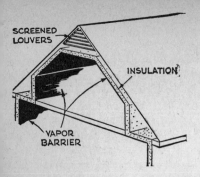

Fig. 16. Louvers and insulation help squash the damage of condensation to vulnerable roof structures.

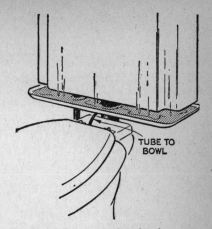

Fig. 17. A shallow pan placed under a water tank to catch dripping water can save your floor.

sation must be corrected, if possible, with better ventilation, air-conditioning or some other means of raising the temperature of the wall. The latter has been known to have been accomplished by simply shifting the position of a hot water heater to a more advantageous position.

BATHROOM FLOORS

During summer months, when humidity is high, water frequently drips on bathroom floors as a result of condensation on the outside surfaces of the toilet tank or bowl. It may occur at other times of the year when someone takes a hot bath, or especially a hot shower. The hot water fills the air with water vapor at a room temperature which is considerably greater than that of the fixtures. When the hot vapor given off by the shower or bath strikes the cooler surfaces around the toilet tank or bowl, it condenses. This may not be troublesome on ceramic tile floors, but on wooden floors it can readily cause decay.

If it is possible to raise the temperature of the water entering the tank, by as much as 15 to 20 degrees, this may prevent condensation or reduce it enough so as to render it harmless. This can be accomplished by putting the tank on a separate system from the remainder of the water supply. The water is then preheated to about room temperature either in a heater in the basement, or by coils placed outdoors or in the attic during the summer. A simple electric heater placed in the tank, which could be controlled by a thermostat, is another possibility. They do not come ready-made but an electric heater like those used to heat tropical fish bowls would serve the purpose. Shallow pans can be bought (Fig. 17), however, which may be slipped under the tank to catch water dripping down after condensation. They have a small drain which leads into the toilet bowl.

CHAPTER 6

TOOLS AND MATERIALS
FOR WATERPROOFING

This chapter contains suggestions on types of tools and materials best suited for certain jobs relating directly or indirectly to dampproofing and waterproofing the home. Many of these may be used for other purposes, too. Naturally, the homeowner will want to have other tools for other types of jobs around the house, as well. This is merely offered as a guide, so that repair work and construction connected with keeping the house free from water may be undertaken with some knowledge of the essential tools and materials.

Hammer

A homeowner's tool kit should contain a claw hammer (Fig. 1), for use with a cold chisel when cleaning out masonry before plugging holes and weak spots. The hammer should be selected on the basis of weight and balance. Sizes vary according to the weight of the head. The face, or part that strikes the object, is on one end, while the opposite part, which may be one of many shapes, is called the peen.

It is important to keep the face of the hammer clean and free from oil and grease. When it is being used to drive nails, a clean hammer will not dirty the walls if it accidentally slips off the head of the nail. When the edge of the face of the hammer chips, it should be ground or filed smooth, so that it will not injure the hand should it slip. The head should be securely attached to the handle; small metal wedges driven into the top of it will help to keep it firmly fixed.

Cold Chisel

Cold chisels (Fig 1), are generally used to enlarge holes and cracks that exist in concrete and other masonry so that repair work can be done on the foundation or other concrete construction. A cold chisel is also used to roughen surfaces which are later to be plastered. It is a most effective tool for removing paint and whitewash from a wall to be plastered. A cold chisel is forged from 6-sided or 8-sided tool steel bars. The cutting edge varies in shape according to use. In almost all work, however, an ordinary duck bill cutting edge is all you need. If holes are to be drilled, a special type of cutting edge, made of a series of sharp edges placed radially, is best suited for the job.

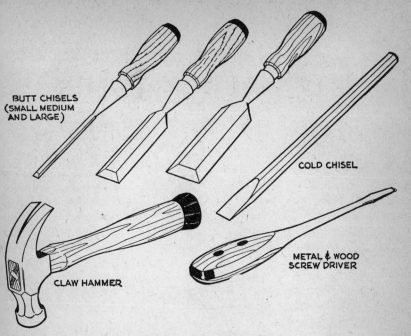

BUTT CHISELS
(SMALL MEDIUM
AND LARGE)

COLD CHISEL

CLAW HAMMER

METAL & WOOD
SCREW DRIVER

Fig. 1. Tools for waterproofing the home.

Screwdriver

In an emergency, a screwdriver (Fig. 1), can be substituted for a cold chisel. It is not recommended, however, if a great deal of work is to be done on brick or concrete, because using the screwdriver in this way will chip the edge and render it useless for its primary function. If a screwdriver is to be used it should be one on which the metal extends to the back of the handle so that the hammer can hit the metal. If an old wood handle is used the hammer will split the wood. The blade of the screwdriver should be kept sharp and should be filed to achieve this purpose, rather than ground. If you grind the blade of a screwdriver the metal may overheat and cause it to lose its temper.

Wood Float

This is an oblong-shaped piece of wood with a wooden handle attached to the back, (Fig. 2). It is used to compact cement plasters before applying finish trowelling. It is also used to level concrete and cement floor finishes after being trowelled.

Plasterer's Trowel

The plasterer's trowel (Fig. 2), is an oblong-shaped piece of spring steel with an "L" shaped handle riveted to the oblong piece. It is used to finish the surface of concrete and cement plaster. When you use this

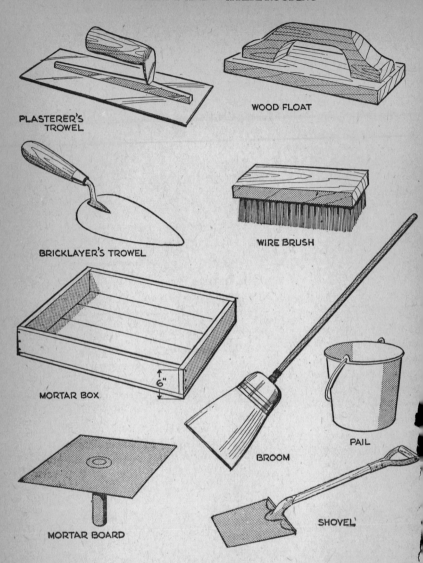

PLASTERER'S TROWEL

WOOD FLOAT

BRICKLAYER'S TROWEL

WIRE BRUSH

MORTAR BOX

6"

PAIL

BROOM

MORTAR BOARD

SHOVEL

Fig. 2. Tools for waterproofing the home.

tool put the weight of your body behind each stroke so that the trowel packs and smooths the concrete simultaneously. If you work concrete unevenly, with alternating light and heavy strokes, too much moisture is removed from the surface and a number of tiny fine or hair cracks

will show after the concrete has
hardened.

Brick Mason's Trowel

This trowel (Fig. 2) is constructed
in a similar manner to that described
for the plasterer's trowel. The shape
of the flat working surface, however,
resembles that of an arrowhead with
the end of the "V" rounded. This
trowel is used to apply mortar when
laying brick or concrete block, and
is also used to point up small openings that may have been cut out to
repair a crack.

Mortar Box

The mortar box (Fig. 2), is a watertight receptacle, oblong in shape,
and about six inches deep. Cement,
sand, and any other aggregate are
dumped into the mortar box in the
proper proportions and mixed together dry to a fairly uniform consistency. The water to go with the
waterproofing, if any, is added in
small quantities, and the mixing is
continued until the entire patch is
of the proper consistency.

Wire Brush

This is a square wooden handpiece
fitted with short wire bristles, (Fig.
2). It is used to brush whitewash and
dirt from a masonry surface leaving
it covered with shallow scratches
that are ideal for receiving cement
plaster.

Whisk Broom

An ordinary whisk broom (Fig. 2),
is a handy gadget to have for dusting

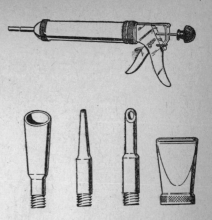

Fig 3. A caulking gun applies pointing
and caulking compounds. Nozzle tips for use
with the gun are available in various
dimensions.

off foundation surfaces so that all
flakes and tiny particles loosened by
chiseling are cleaned out. A whisk
broom is also a very useful tool for
the cement worker, as it may be used
to scratch the surface of fresh cement
plaster so that a second coat can be
applied after the first has set.

Water Bucket or Pail

After cement or mortar has been
mixed, it is necessary to carry it
away in a pail (Fig. 2), where it can
either be dumped directly into the
form as in the case of laying concrete, or kept in the pail while patchwork is being undertaken. The pail
should be thoroughly cleaned after
each use and properly dried so that
it will not rust or crack. Never use a
pail as a footstool as this weakens the
metal and is extremely dangerous
because the bottom may give, or slip

out from under. Pails are sold in various sizes. A number is generally embossed on the bottom indicating the number of quarts containable.

Mortar Board

When you are repairing plaster, a mortar board (Fig. 2), or hawk, is handy for holding small amounts of

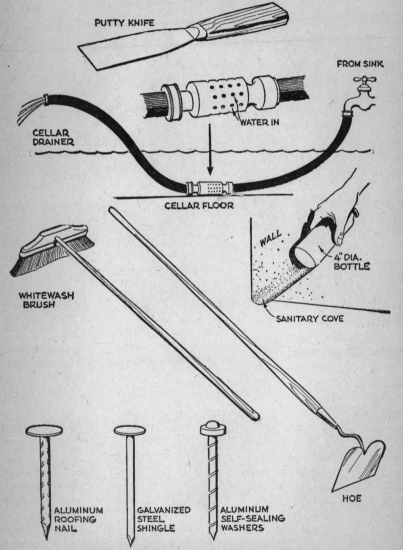

PUTTY KNIFE

FROM SINK

WATER IN

CELLAR DRAINER

CELLAR FLOOR

WALL

4" DIA. BOTTLE

WHITEWASH BRUSH

SANITARY COVE

ALUMINUM ROOFING NAIL

GALVANIZED STEEL SHINGLE

ALUMINUM SELF-SEALING WASHERS

HOE

Fig. 4. Tools for waterproofing the home.

plaster so that it will not be necessary to take it out of the pail or other container. This is especially convenient if it is necessary to work on a ladder as it might be dangerous to place a large quantity of plaster on the ladder. A mortar board is light and easy to hold. It is square with a round handle inserted in the center of the square.

Shovel

The best and most useful shovel (Fig. 2), for cement work is a straight, square-edged one not unlike a garden spade. In fact, a garden spade will serve well. You can shovel cement from its storage pile to the mortar box, and you can, to some extent, mix the ingredients in the mortar box. The same shovel can be used for excavating around foundations, digging a trench to lay a drain line, or any other earth removal operation. Shovels, like all mechanic's tools, should be carefully cleaned after using, and dried before storing.

Caulking Gun

This is the instrument (Fig 3), used for filling cracks by means of a plastic cement called a caulking compound. The caulking gun is something like a grease gun since it literally "shoots" the compound into the opening under pressure and is able to fill the entire depth of the crack. The gun has a cylindrical metal barrel about two inches in diameter and seven inches long on the inside. The compound is forced through the nozzle by a piston which is moved by a handgrip or lever.

Most nozzles have round openings ⅛" to ¼" in diameter; some have triangular openings which are ¼" to ½" on a side. A putty knife can be used to fill the gun, but it is much simpler to get cartridges of the caulking compound which insert easily into the gun. Two or 3 average windows in masonry walls, or 5 or 6 average windows in frame construction, can be caulked with a quart of compound. Press the handgrip of the gun while moving the nozzle at a uniform rate along the crack being filled, making certain to hold the gun close enough so that the bevelled or tapered end (about ½" wide) can be used to indicate that the compound has been pushed as far in as possible. Keep the wood wet so that the nozzle will slide more easily, and use it to smooth the compound. Different sizes of nozzles can be purchased with the caulking gun.

Putty Knife

Although not as fast as a caulking gun, and somewhat tiring to use, a putty knife (Fig. 4), is nevertheless a valuable tool for glazing and patching up holes and small cavities in the masonry. It will do what a caulking gun does, though it is clumsier.

Cellar Drainer

This is a siphon type of pump, (Fig. 4). When connected with a hose to a faucet it is used to remove water from a cellar floor or pit, or to keep the water down during a waterproofing job. It is a small brass fitting with a hose attached at each end through which the water passes.

Hoe

An ordinary garden hoe (Fig. 4), will usually suffice for mixing mortar and cement.

Cove Trowel

Wherever cement plaster on a wall joins the floor topping, the intersection should be rounded to form a sanitary cove. Steel trowels can be obtained to finish these round intersections. However, these are not necessary. The same effect can be produced with the side of a round bottle (Fig. 4), and an excellent finish of the intersection between the floor and wall can be made. The bottle should measure about three or four inches in diameter.

Brushes

For most purposes an inexpensive whitewash brush (Fig 4), can be used. In every instance it is important that the brushes be cleaned before using and carefully washed out and left clean after use. The method of washing depends largely on the nature of the material that has been applied with the brush. The black dampproofing paints will require a solvent, such as gasoline, to remove the tar and asphalt. Cement paints can be washed out with water.

Nails

Nails (Fig 4), are important in certain types of construction — especially where there is a "dry wall" construction. In such cases, when moisture gets on the inside of the wall, it may be drawn to the head of the nail where it will condense and sometimes cause streaks to run down the side of the wall. The head of an ordinary steel nail may also rust under such conditions. An aluminum nail, or other stainless type is generally more satisfactory, even though it may be a little more expensive. Nails which are seriously affected by water will not only rust but they will also lose their effectiveness.

MATERIALS

The home mechanic should know something about the materials used in waterproofing, both as a guide, in case he needs to perform a waterproofing job himself, and also to properly judge the condition of construction in his own home. The various applications of these material will be explained more fully in later chapters dealing with specific methods of waterproofing.

Concrete

Many kinds of repairs about the house are best accomplished with concrete. Sidewalks and basement floors are but two examples. Concrete is not an expensive building material and the non-professional can do satisfactory work with it if he experiments before taking on a complicated job. *See Chapter 1, Facts About Concrete.*

Mixing Concrete

The first step is to mix the sand, cement, and gravel dry, until they are evenly mixed and uniform in color (Fig. 5).

Fig. 5. The first step in mixing concrete is to mix the sand, cement ,and gravel dry, until the mass is evenly mixed and uniform in color.

If you are adding a waterproofing compound for integral waterproofing follow the instructions on the water-proofing container as to the amount of water to be added. If you are making plain concrete without a waterproofing compound, just add enough water to be able to handle the concrete from the mortar box to the forms.

Mortar

Brick, tile, and other masonry units are held together and supported by mortar which is applied when it is in a paste or plastic condition to the spaces or joints between these substances. This paste hardens and, consequently, serves as a binder for brick and other masonry units. It is made from hydrated lime, portland cement, and sand, mixed with water. There are three principal types of mortar: cement-lime mortar, lime mortar, and cement mortar. Cement-lime mortar may be used for practically all masonry above the ground. Lime mortar is used when loads are light and the weather conditions are not severe. It is used only above ground. Cement mortar is used for all masonry which is below ground, and can also be used in exterior walls, chimneys, and generally, wherever crushing forces exist. In all waterproofing a portland cement mortar should be used.

Mixing Mortar

Spread sand evenly over a mixing board or in the bottom of a mixing box, (Fig 6). Then put the cement and dry lime, if used, on top of the sand. Use a hoe to mix these dry ingredients until they make a smooth, uniform appearance. Finally, add

SMOOTH OUT
SAND

Fig. 6. To mix mortar, spread sand evenly in the bottom of a mixing board, place the cement and dry lime on top of the sand, mix until you obtain a smooth, uniform appearance, and finally add water so that a paste is formed.

water to the dry mixture so that a paste is formed. Care should be observed in adding water because the point at which you have too much is difficult to observe. At one moment, while water is being added, it may seem as though the mixture is still very dry. Yet the addition of just a little more water may make it altogether too soft. *See also Mixing Mortar under Chapter 2.*

If the mortar contains portland cement do not add any more water to the mixture than can be applied within a 30-minute period because after that time the mixture begins to set. A straight lime mortar does not have to be used quite so soon. When you can no longer dent the mortar or mark it with your thumbnail it has reached its final hardness. Mortar can be colored with any non-organic mineral color such as you might use in paints.

Mortar is extremely valuable as a material for patchwork and re-pointing, which is extremely important in preventing dampness and seepage in the home. Exterior surfaces should be examined periodically and cracks and holes filled with fresh mortar to maintain a watertight surface.

Portland Cement

This is used in making all concrete and mortar, and therefore is an essential part of such mixtures. Actually, it is the binding portion of the mixture which serves to hold the other materials together and create a water-tight composition. *See Chapter 1.*

Keene's Cement

This is a type of hard, quick-setting plaster used on bathroom walls or on the walls of shower stalls where it is necessary to protect the wall from exposure to large amounts of water.

Asphalt and Tar Paint

These are applied on the back of plywood and similar finishes on the inside of basement walls to act as a vapor barrier. Several quarts should be used to provide a smooth glossy surface which will help prevent condensation and dampness. Since neither asphalt nor tar paint are especially decorative, they are not recommended for use on the exposed side of the wall. They are also used as foundation coatings and, when used in connection with tar paper or felt, they act as a binder and damp-proofer in membrane waterproofing. Special paints which remain tacky are used as a plaster bond. These paints generally have a solvent which evaporates easily. They should therefore be kept tightly covered when not in use, (Fig. 7). Otherwise the surface will dry in the can and the balance of the paint will be worthless.

Tar Paper

These are sheets of heavy brown paper similar to those sometimes used to provide safe storage for woolen clothing from moths. Tar paper can be used in constructing a tile drain and also in connection with vapor barriers and membrane waterproofing.

Burlap

Ordinary burlap has many uses around the house and can be used effectively in making a cover over the joints in a tile drain which, while it permits water to go through, at the same time acts as a filter to prevent dirt and dust from clogging the drain.

Putty

This is made with white lead, boiled linseed oil, and whiting. First, put dry whiting on a flat surface. Then take a putty knife and make a stiff paste by working in the white lead with the oil. Cover your hands with dry whiting, pick up the whole mixture, and massage it in your hands as though you were handling dough. Add extra whiting if the mass appears to be too soft and sticky on

Fig. 7. Asphalt and tar paints generally have a solvent which evaporates easily. They should therefore be kept tightly covered when not in use.

the fingers. Add boiled linseed oil if the form is so dry that it separates into separate lumps. Once you have obtained a sufficient quantity of well-massaged or kneaded material, put it down on a hard surface and pound it with a mallet to keep the mix. When submerged in water this putty will keep indefinitely and improve with age. Greater adhesiveness can be achieved and putty can be made harder when it is finally set if a little spar varnish, exterior varnish, or good floor varnish is

Fig. 8. Caulking material is the best means of closing cracks between different structural materials.

added. Be sure to put in some more whiting, however, to prevent the mixture from becoming too thin.

If the putty is to be used for filling in and smoothing cracks and other irregularities in the masonry outdoors, be sure that enough varnish or oil is added to make the mixture fairly soft. Putty is also suitable for holding glass windows and doors, and patching up all types of cracks and holes in masonry.

Swedish putty is the general name applied to a variety of mixtures of putty used for filling large cracks or splits in floors or walls and for covering any rough spots.

Caulking Compound

This is a plastic cement used for filling cracks around windows or between joints where water may penetrate. It is used also to stop leaks at points where wood framing rests on masonry foundations, or at points where pipes or electrical wiring come through building walls. It is a material which remains elastic for long periods and sticks very strongly to wood, metal, brick, concrete, and other building materials.

Three different types of caulking are available. The first is a knifing grade compound, which is stiff enough to be applied with an ordinary knife, a putty knife, or even a small trowel. Then there is gun gray, which is usually applied by means of a caulking gun, and thirdly, there is caulking tape, which is the compound in strip form applied by merely pressing into place.

Caulking material, it should be emphasized, is the best means of closing cracks between different structural materials, (Fig. 8). Mortar, cement, and putty cannot be used for such purposes because when they dry out the expansion and contraction which is inherent when two different types of materials come together, causes them to crack and crumble.

Waterproofing Compound

This comes in powder, paste, and liquid forms. Differences among them are largely a matter of opinion. It is important, however, to purchase a waterproofing compound from a reliable manufacturer because there are some waterproofers on the market made by irresponsible companies who claim outlandish and impossible results for their products.

Felt

Felt in sheet form is used in the membrane system of waterproofing. It is composed of pulp or cotton rags with a little wool. The wool makes the felt open and spongy and increases its ability to absorb moisture. The sheets usually come in 36" widths and are saturated with asphalt or tar. Asphalt felt is a soft felt, while tar felt is regarded as a hard felt. Felt is sold by weight or roll and comes in standard thicknesses. Its quality is designated by a number, the higher numbers being heavier.

Roofing Paper

This usually consists of pieces of felt or roll roofing used to patch up leaks in roofs. Roofing paper is generally needed when asbestos, cement, slate roofs, and flat tile roofs become leaky. This happens when an individual piece of roofing loosens because of the failure of nails to hold it in place, or due to some accident which breaks one of the roofing pieces. In such cases the broken or loosened piece is removed and the roofing paper is put in its place.

Shingles

In order to replace wood shingles or composition shingles that show a tendency to curl or lift up, and therefore encourage leakage, particularly when there is a strong wind or during a rainstorm, it is a good idea to keep a couple of extra shingles on hand. If the house is new there may be shingles left over from the roofing which you can use for such purposes. Otherwise, it might be advisable to buy a few and have them ready when needed for repair work.

CHAPTER 7

WATERPROOFING AND DAMPPROOFING METHODS

It is extremely important for the homeowner to know something about the waterproofing and dampproofing methods used on his home. If a water condition should develop, where one has not previously existed, the cause may possibly be deterioration of some component part of the waterproofing method used when the house was constructed. Many low cost houses, for example, depend upon nothing more than an asphalt or tar coating brushed or trowelled onto the outside surface of the walls. These coatings are frequently soluble in wet earth and may gradually be absorbed by the surrounding earth, disappearing completely from the surface of the wall. This could take place two or three years after the waterproofing was applied.

If the homeowner knows that a membrane waterproofing system was employed on foundation walls he can logically reason that leakage on one of these walls may be due to a hole or opening in the membrane. The most frequent cause for such openings is a slight movement of the foundation. This would occur when the building settles. An indication of this condition is a crack in the foundation walls. The crack should be examined carefully to determine the direction

of settlement. If the crack is wider at the top than at the bottom it is obvious that the wall moved a greater distance, several feet away from the crack, than directly under it. On the other hand, if the crack is wider at the bottom than at the top it is evident that the wall moved a greater distance, directly under the crack, than several feet away from it, (Fig.).

In either instance, movement of the wall tends to tear the membrane waterproofing. It is then necessary to patch up the hole to prevent further leakage. To repair this rupture an excavation around the outside of the foundation wall must be dug to expose the membrane waterproofing at this point. If there is a tear in the paper used, it can be repaired easily. First, thoroughly clean the surface where the rupture occurs and then apply a saturating coat of tar or asphalt. This will tend to fill the crevice and also act as a binder for the paper which is to be applied as a patch. A piece of heavy building paper or building felt may be used for the patch. It should be pressed against the wet asphalt or tar and painted over with the same black material. Sometimes a stain appears on a wall some distance from where the actual break in the membrane waterproofing took place. This happens when there is no opening nearby in the wall through which the water can leak. It then spreads out in back of the membrane and runs along the wall until it finds a weak spot where it can get through. Such a condition can be treated as in the first instance, but the hole in the membrane will have to be sought some distance from where the stains on the inside wall appear and a longer excavation trench will be needed. Where the type of waterproofing is not known, however, needless time and expense may be spent in trying to solve the problem.

ffect of Installation

Alterations or improvements, such s putting in a new plumbing system, ten require additional pipes. The fect such an installation may have n the waterproofing system must be carefully considered from all angles. New pipes put through a wall that has been made water-tight by membrane waterproofing will puncture the system. If they are installed above the water line, however, trouble may be avoided, even if the membrane waterproofing is pierced. The possibility of leakage due to hydrostatic pressure is less of a problem the higher up you go on foundation walls. If a water condition results, however, the membrane system should be repaired. The pipe is then carefully sealed at the hole through the membrane waterproofing so that water cannot enter around the pipe. This is accomplished by

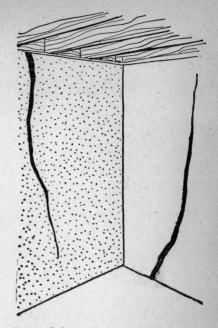

Fig. I. If the crack in a foundation wall is wider at the top, the wall moved a greater distance away from the crack than directly under it. If the crack is wider at the bottom, then the wall moved a greater distance directly under the crack than away from it.

wrapping a tar paper or felt around the pipe and spreading the end in contact with the membrane waterproofing, (Fig. 2). The entire patch is then thoroughly swabbed with tar or asphalt. Any installation which punctures the membrane waterproofing system will have to be handled in the same way. Even when decorative work is being done in a cellar it is important to know what type of waterproofing system has been used so that merely driving nails in a wall will not puncture the waterproofing and bring on leaks.

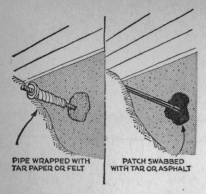

PIPE WRAPPED WITH
TAR PAPER OR FELT

PATCH SWABBED
WITH TAR OR ASPHALT

Fig. 2. New plumbing installed below the water line should be wrapped in tar paper or felt, and spread toward the membrane waterproofing. It must then be swabbed with tar or asphalt.

Signs of Waterproofing

Usually the builder will be glad to supply this information, but in the case of old houses, it may be difficult to find out what had been done originally to waterproof and dampproof. In such a situation homeowners should look for certain signs, such as a black substance on the outer basement walls which indicates the presence of asphalt paint or tar. This can be determined if you dig down about a foot below the ground level on the outside of the foundation wall. If a membrane waterproofing is used you should see either the tar paper or felt. In the absence of either paper or felt, you may find simply a black surface coating. If there is no evidence of black waterproofing on the outside this indicates that there was no membrane waterproofing system used. There may have been a black coating, however, but this could dis-

appear if it was absorbed by the earth. It is possible, too, that the waterproofing consisted of a cement plaster applied on the outside surface of the foundation wall. This would be visible.

If an examination of the outside shows no evidence of waterproofing, black applications or cement plaster, foundations may have been waterproofed in one of the following manners: Waterproofing may have been used through the mass of the concrete walls, if they are concrete, or an integral waterproofing may have been used in the cement mortar of a block or brick foundation wall. In either case, a leak on the inside will occur directly opposite the opening on the outside. If no waterproofing has been used on the wall it is just possible that the builder depended entirely upon a drainage system to carry the water away from the foundation before it could rise high enough to cause trouble (Fig. 3). Such drains are found at the level of the footings. It is not necessary, however, to dig down through the footing to determine if drainage is installed. Drains are useful only when they run to some low point where the water can run off. It is generally easy to find such openings either at the curb where the drains run into the street or, if the house sets up on a terrace, the drain outlets may be visible at some low point in the terrace itself. If no outlets can be found there is a possibility that footing drains have been run off to a dry well installed somewhere on the ground.

When planting shrubbery or a garden around the sides of your house consider the way in which water is drained away from the house so you may avoid interference with the drainage system, or in some other way cause a new condition which will bring on a water problem. If you are determined to have your garden regardless, then you will at least know what precautions must be taken to protect the house from water.

If no signs of waterproofing are visible on the outside it is possible that the waterproofing may have been integrated in the construction of the building, or it may have been applied on the inside surfaces with adequate drainage provided to relieve the pressure. Below the ground you cannot identify integral waterproofing in a concrete wall or floor, but you can recognize cement plaster applied directly to the inside surface of the foundation walls. Membrane waterproofing is never used on the inside surfaces.

The discussion of the principal waterproofing and dampproofing methods which follows will be supplemented in more detail in sections relating to particular problems and specific ways and means of correcting them. The following information should provide a good introduction, however, to a proper understanding of usual techniques and methods used.

INTEGRAL SYSTEM

When a construction material, such as concrete, is mixed with a waterproofing compound along with the other ingredients necessary for

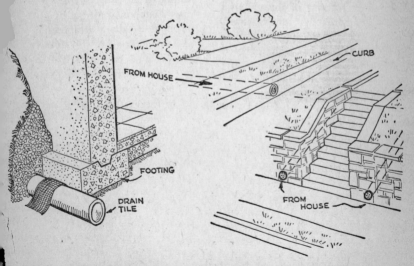

Fig. 3. Some builders depend entirely upon a drainage system to carry the water away before it can rise high enough to cause trouble. Such drains are found at the level of the footing.

Fig. 4. Powder and paste waterproofing must be stirred up continually in order to keep them in suspension and insure uniform distribution.

Powder and paste waterproofings must be stirred up continuously in order to keep them in suspension and insure more uniform distribution, (Fig. 4). Liquid waterproofing, however, mixes with water and gives a uniform solution. Some integral waterproofings are water repellents, the theory being that if these are incorporated in the cement mixtures they will produce a finished product which will shed the water. This type of waterproofing actually weakens the resulting cement mixtures. Other integral waterproofing reacts chemically with the cement itself to form a dense, impermeable mass through which the water cannot penetrate. This type is preferred bcause waterproofing which produces a dense cement mixture increases its strength.

Once the concrete or mortar has hardened and set, the waterproofing compound it contains will prevent water from penetrating it in any way. In other words, waterproofing has been made a part of the construction material and, to put it still another way, the construction material has become waterproof.

The integral method is best used when new construction is being put up, but it can also be employed if a new concrete floor must be laid in the basement, or if an inside wall is to be covered with a plaster, in which an integral waterproofing may be incorporated. In a sense, mortar which has been integrated with a waterproofing compound, used for patching and repairing outside masonry, is also an example of waterproofing by means of the integral method.

its composure, the waterproofing compound then becomes an inherent part or integral part of the material produced. Concrete, for example, made in the normal way, is always porous and can be waterproofed simply by adding a waterproofing compound to the mixture before it sets. This is true also of mortar, plaster and other construction materials which are made by mixing a combination of ingredients, one of which is always portland cement. Portland cement is essential because it acts as a binder to hold the sand, stone and gravel together.

The waterproofing compound may be a powder, paste or a liquid. The only difference is the ease with which they are mixed into the concrete or other material. In this respect, liquids are inclined to be easier to handle.

Concrete Roofs

Concrete roofs integrally water-proofed are used very successfully, especially on garages where no particular architectural effect is required. The integral method can also be used in the base of a shower bath or even for the entire bathroom floor, (Fig. 5). Moreover, it has proven extremely effective in waterproofing kitchen floors, especially if there is a storeroom underneath. Water spilling from dish washing machines or other appliances sometimes leaks through the kitchen floor into the space below.

Wherever any cement work is to be done, the addition of integral waterproofing will produce a finished product that has the additional quality of being waterproofed. This applies to driveways, outside cellar steps, window sills and any other cement construction including the many foundation jobs previously mentioned. If you are building your own home it is generally easier and more effective to employ the integral system of waterproofing than any other.

If you have an integral waterproofing system, for example, on the foundation walls, and you want to make a hole through it to run pipes or something similar (Fig. 6), all you have to do is plug up the openings around the hole. This can be done with a suitable mastic or with a portland cement mixture, and the repair can always be made on the inside where it is accessible. On the other hand, if a membrane waterproofing had been used it is a more difficult matter to seal the rupture and this must always be done on the outside where it is more inaccessible.

Integral Dampproofing

A very effective dampproof paint can be made by mixing portland cement into a solution of water and any liquid waterproofing which reacts chemically with portland cement. The usual proportion is to mix one part of the liquid waterproofing with three parts of water and to stir enough portland cement into this

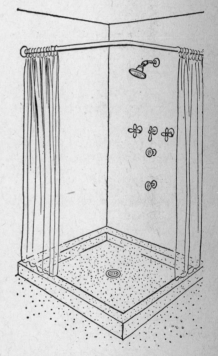

Fig. 5. The integral method of waterproofing, in which the waterproofing is part of the cement work in which it is incorporated, is excellent for shower bath, bathroom, and basement floors.

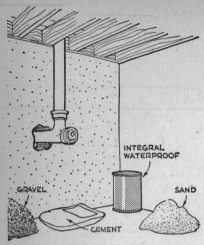

INTEGRAL WATERPROOFED WALL CAN BE
PATCHED FROM THE INSIDE

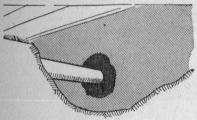

MEMBRANE WATERPROOFED WALL MUST
BE PATCHED FROM THE OUTSIDE

Fig. 6. Plugging of foundation walls through
which pipes run can be done with a suitable
mastic or portland cement from inside or
outside.

solution to form the consistency of a
heavy paint. This can then be
brushed or sprayed on the outside of
masonry walls above the ground to
prevent rain penetration through the
walls. A dampproof paint of this
kind produces a gray surface. Mineral water colors may be added to
the cement if a colored effect is
wanted. Red and buff are the most
satisfactory cement colors. Green and

blues should be avoided because the
chemicals used in these colors
weaken the cement and will rub off.
If further decoration is wanted any
outdoor paint can be applied to a
cement dampproof paint after the
cement paint has set. In new construction work, such a dampproof
cement paint is frequently used on
the inside of brick walls to prevent
moisture from penetrating through
to the finished plaster. A portland
cement paint made with white portland cement, instead of the ordinary
gray portland cement, makes an excellent finish for inside basement
walls, or the inside of garage walls
where a clean, light effect is desired.

MEMBRANE SYSTEM

This is a more complicated and
detailed method of waterproofing
than the integral, and requires considerably more care in its application.
It involves the sandwiching of construction material between membrane, or tar paper and felt, in ord
to prevent water leakage and see
age, (Fig. 7). The principle of th
membrane system is to wrap up the
foundation of the house in a waterproof paper or felt. The effectiveness
of this method is very much handi-
capped if the contour or shape of the
foundation requires a great many
bends of this wrapping. You can
visualize the simplicity of wrapping
a shoe box in paper and the difficulty
of wrapping a package containing a
variety of shapes such as the grocer
encounters when he tries to make a
package with boxes, cans and bottles

Something is likely to poke a hole through the latter more readily than a uniform package such as the shoe box. The same difficulty presents itself when trying to wrap up a foundation.

A very old method of employing the membrane system was the use of so-called batts and blanket. The batts consisted of wool or cotton prepared in sheet form and placed above and below a concrete wall or floor. They tended to absorb water and prevent its passage into the construction material. Such moisture that would get through was then absorbed by the membrane on the inside surface. Today, the sheets used are made either of felt, treated with asphalt, tar paper similarly treated, or asbestos felt likewise saturated with a bitumen, and are applied only to the outside. The bitumens, such as asphalt and pitch, are used because they have very elastic and binding characteristics and are not inclined to be weakened on contact with water. They work well when applied felts or fabrics whose purpose is absorb the moisture and prevent it from reaching the interior of the house, either through walls, roofs or floors.

Vapor Barriers

Vapor barriers, which are used to protect insulation material and help prevent condensation, are constructed along the same principle as the membrane waterproofing system. They are, however, installed inside the wall, generally between the outside masonry wall and the inside fin-

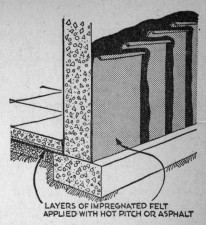

LAYERS OF IMPREGNATED FELT
APPLIED WITH HOT PITCH OR ASPHALT

Fig. 7. Membrane waterproofing involves the sandwiching of construction material between membrane, or tar paper and felt, to prevent water leakage and seepage.

ish plaster. The membrane method is used only as a means of waterproofing below the ground or on the roof where hydrostatic pressure is a factor.

When a home has been waterproofed with the membrane system, new pipes or light fixtures can cause a break in the system when they are installed. An easy way of understanding the difference between the integral method and the membrane is to remember that membrane waterproofing (Fig. 8), is applied to the surface and, although it may be accomplished during new construction, it is a separate operation, whereas the integral technique is always a part of the cement work in which it is incorporated.

In considering the construction of a new home it is important to remember that both the integral method and the membrane method will produce dry foundations if they are properly used. The cost, however, is considerably less for the integral method than for the membrane method. Furthermore, additions to the foundations can be more easily attached where the integral method is used than where the membrane is used, because it is easier to make a tight joint between new masonry and old with the integral method than with the membrane method.

If the homeowner desires to install a membrane waterproofing system around the foundation of his house himself there are certain considera-

tions which should be kept in mind. Foremost is that an excavation must be dug down to the footings, and it must be wide enough for a man to work in. The cost of this excavation will often exceed the cost for the complete waterproofing job.

Surface Applications

Another method which sometimes provides temporary relief from water conditions and is essentially a damp-proofing, is the application of so-called waterproof paints to exterior and interior surfaces. This method is not as reliable or efficient as the preceding two, but when it is im-

Fig. 8. Membrane waterproofing is applied to the surface, and although it may be accomplished during new construction it is a separate operation.

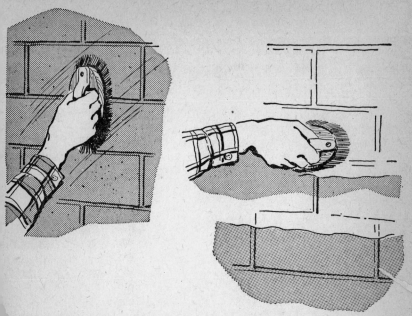

Fig. 9. Preparation of interior and exterior surfaces is important when using waterproofing paints. Walls must be thoroughly cleaned to achieve the best results.

possible or impractical to employ either the integral or membrane system, a surface coating may be applied as a temporary waterproofing and permanent dampproofing remedy.

Emphasis must be made of the fact that there are some products that are on the market for which irresponsible and extravagant claims are made. Unless a reliable product from a reputable manufacturer is purchased, the results of applying a waterproofing paint are likely to be entirely unsatisfactory, costly and exasperating.

Reliable waterproofing paints, however, which do not make exorbitant claims, may be applied directly to the interior and exterior surfaces as an effective means of preventing seepage. They are not considered satisfactory by themselves, however, as a means of preventing leakage due to pressure. One of the most important things to bear in mind in applying waterproofing paints, moreover, is to follow the directions of the manufacturer precisely and to be particularly diligent about preparing the surface properly before applying the waterproofing or dampproofing. Results will depend almost entirely on how carefully the paint has been applied. Walls must be thoroughly cleaned in order to achieve best results, (Fig. 9).

Bituminous paints, such as coal tar, are often used as a surface coating for dampproofing purposes. Because of their appearance, however, they are not recommended for application on surfaces which must be decorative, but they can be used effectively on inside surfaces and foundation walls if they are to be covered by plywood or similar material. Special asphalt paints may be purchased which are used for the double purpose of dampproofing the wall and to receive the finished white plaster. This type of dampproof paint is generally designated as a plaster bond. It may be used without reservation on vertical walls. It should never be used on ceilings, however, because the weight of the plaster may break the bond and cause the plaster to drop off.

Other surface coatings suitable for temporary waterproofing and efficient dampproofing are cement mixtures containing suitable integral waterproofing; lean and rich mortars; powdered metal, usually comprised of iron filings and salammoniac; the Sylvestor process, which is a soap and alum solution; and paraffin.

Caulking

Caulking materials are never employed for a complete waterproofing job. They are simply used to seal openings between masonry walls and wood or metal insertions such as window frames and conduits. These materials are of a putty-like consistency. They are pliable and can be forced into crevices with any blunt tool. They usually harden from exposure to air.

Transparent Dampproofing

Masonry walls above the ground which are porous frequently need to be dampproofed in a manner which will not change the architectural effect. This can be accomplished with a transparent liquid with an oil or paraffin base. Some of these transparent dampproofings have a tendency to darken the color, just a shade, and consequently should never be used on white surfaces which you wish to remain as they are.

The application and variations of these methods noted briefly in this chapter are the basis for all waterproofing and dampproofing operations designed to prevent water leakage and seepage. The chapters which follow will deal with individual problems in various sections of the house and describe, in detail, methods for solving the difficulties.

CHAPTER 8

IS THE BASEMENT DRY?

A basement is a tremendous asset to a home if it is dry. It will then be completely satisfactory for storage purposes and for housing heating equipment and other appliances. In addition, it may also be used to provide space for a workshop, playroom and even extra living quarters. It has an important bearing on the life and value of the home. But before taking any steps to prevent dampness and leakage, first consider the various purposes for which the basement may be used. Then decide if the expense of repairing a leakage or dampness condition is warranted.

Adds to Value of Home

Water in the basement will cause woodwork to rot and metallic surfaces to rust. This weakens the framework of the house and deteriorates furniture and woodwork upstairs. Walls are discolored and wallpaper may peel or buckle, (Fig. 1). Increased maintenance and repair costs result and the life of the home is shortened.

Importance of Waterproofing

Once it has been decided how the basement is to be used, the necessity for waterproofing and dampproofing should be determined. Sometimes the cost of such operations will outweigh the value of using the basement for a particular purpose. If dampness interferes with healthy and comfortable living, however, remedial measures must be taken.

It is about one-tench as expensive to properly waterproof a basement or foundation when the house is being built than to attempt to remedy dampness and leakage later on. Home buyers should therefore carefully check the condition of the cellar before making their purchase. Ask the builder what steps were taken to prevent water and dampness. In case trouble develops later on, this information may offer a clue as to why the waterproofing system failed. It will also provide a starting place from which you may proceed to correct the condition. If it is an old house, find out if the basement is usable throughout the year and inquire as to what waterprofing steps were taken in the original construction, or since the original construction was completed.

In homes where basements have been habitually dry, anticipated changes or additions to the construction should not be undertaken without regard to their possible affect on the condition of the basement. New plumbing or fixtures, or even redecoration in the basement, may upset a watertight condition.

Basements are more vulnerable to water penetration than any other part of the house. They are subjected to leakage, seepage, capillarity, and condensation. Water which gets down around the sides of the foundation frequently forms pools under the basement floor. The resulting water pressure is often so powerful it can lift and crack the floor and cause serious water problems in the cellar, (Fig. 2). Roofs are sometimes subject to this hydrostatic pressure, but it is always an extremely serious threat to a basement.

Where the basement is constructed of concrete, or some other type of masonry material, there is every reason to believe that it will be completely watertight. Nevertheless, the possibility of improper mixing of the concrete or the use of inferior materials, plus faulty workmanship, may create openings or cracks which will permit water to get through. This is particularly true today when homes are being built very rapidly and the choice of materials and the standard of workmanship is often of poor quality. When joints are improperly sealed they provide space for water to get through. Moreover, if the concrete mixture is too porous, dampness due to capillarity occurs. As a result of these factors, water penetration is always a potent force to be reckoned with in the basement.

While it is much easier to take into account the location of a home before buying, it is also a factor to be considered in preventing dampness in the basement of an old home. The soil, for example, offers

Fig. 1. A water condition in the basement will cause walls to discolor and wallpaper to peel or buckle.

a clue as to drainage possibilities. If the soil is open and porous so that air and water are easily admitted, the drainage problem will often take care of itself. This is true of sands, gravels, and loams. In less porous soils, however, the water will tend to collect and form pressure pools under the foundation.

CAUSES OF DAMPNESS

Rain water which collects outside the foundation walls and exercises pressure against the masonry and basement floor may cause dampness or leakage in the cellar. This water may come from the roof when there is improper means of draining it away from the foundation. Then,

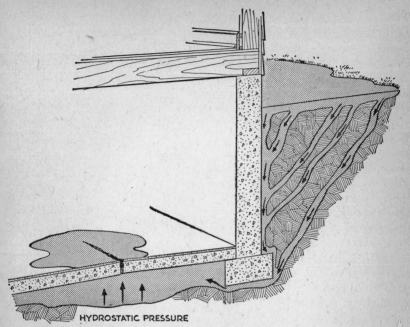

Fig. 2. Water which gets down around the sides of the foundation frequently forms po ls under the basement floor. The resulting hydrostatic pressure lifts and cracks the floor cau ig water problems.

too, when the ground beneath the surface of the earth is extremely wet due to undrground streams, moisure may rise from the soil and penerate into the basement by means of capillarity.

Humidity in the air will cause condensation on basement walls and floors when there is a temperature change. This usually occurs in warm weather when a kind of "sweating" es place on concrete and metallic surfaces. It is especially noticeable on cold water pipes or cold basement walls when the water vapor in the warm air condenses on the cold surfaces. This may cause drops of water on the wall or pipes to drip down on

the floor and create dampness and other water problems. Leaks from plumbing are also a factor in the basement, although they are usually easy to identify and repair. Dense masses of vines, shrubbery and trees surrounding the outside of a house may collect water and direct it against the foundation wall. This water will then penetrate through the pores in the masonry by means of capillary action. Occasionally, a water problem may occur when an inside drain in the basement floor gets clogged up and the water backs up and floods the floor. The ways and means of preventing leakage and other water conditions brought on in these various ways will be dealt with in detail in this chapter.

Points of Penetration

Poor materials and faulty workmanship in construction are frequently responsible for excessive porosity of walls and floors which makes it possible for water to seep through them. Cracks in the masonry walls or floor are another source of openings through which water can enter, (Fig. 3). These are usually due to building settlement, or pressure of ground water around the foundation. At all seams or joints of juncture between walls and floors and footings, and where iron or lally columns penetrate through the floor, the possibility of tiny openings is great because the construction is not continuous. The same applies to open-

ings where pipes, conduits, windows steps and door frames go through walls and floors. New conditions o. developments, such as a converted heater, a fireplace or new window may also offer opportunities for water to break through the outside of the basement.

DAMPNESS AND LEAKAGE

Water and dampness appear in the basement in four principal forms. leakage, seepage, moisture due to capillarity and condensation. These occur individually or there may be a combination of two or all four, as sources of trouble. It is extremely important, however, to determine the form involved before attempting any remedy. Measures taken to prevent leakage will generally help stop seep-

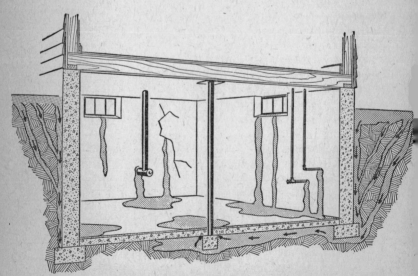

Fig. 3. Cracks in the masonry walls or floor are points of penetration through which water can enter the basement.

age and capillarity as well, but condensation requires a completely different approach.

Leakage

This is the easiest form of water and dampness to identify. It is simply the flow of water through visible openings that may occur in the basement floor or walls. Usually it takes place during, or after, a heavy rain. Water gathers on the surface next to the foundation wall. It runs down between the wall and the ground and finds openings or weak spots where it manages to get through. Such places are often present at points where the continuity of construction has been broken; where conduits or pipes enter the building, or at joints where the floor and wall come together. Also, when the foundation settles, it frequently causes a crack which acts as an opening for leakage too.

It is important to understand that this rain water does not strike the walls of the basement directly, since they are submerged. It is collected in the ground alongside the walls, or it may run down and gather beneath the floor. The body of water formed is capable of exerting great pressure. It is this pressure which forces the water against the walls and through existing openings. If a large quantity of water collects alongside foundation walls or beneath the floor, the pressure is tremendous. Consequently, even if there are no openings or holes through which this water can pass into the basement, the force it exerts may be so strong

that it will be able to crack the concrete floor.

Leakage will frequently result in standing water in the cellar. It renders the entire basement damp and often causes dampness and water conditions in the floors above. It may flood the basement and rise high enough to put the fire out in a furnace or heater. The only way it can then be removed is to pump it out.

The logical approach to preventing leakage would appear to be simply to seal up the openings and plug up the holes where the water comes through. This is often effective if the pressure is not very great. But if it is, new openings will be discovered or created in different places.

Consequently, the source of the leakage must be traced. If the water can be kept away from the foundation walls and floor the leakage may be eliminated. This calls for an examination of the drainage system. Oftentimes a clogged downspout which has caused roof water to overflow the gutter and run down over the outside of the house wall collect around the foundation wall and seep in through openings. In such a case, removing the debris and cleaning out the downspout will be all that is necessary to direct the water away from the foundation. The purpose of proper drainage, therefore, is to permit the water to run off before it can collect around the foundation.

If the basement floor is below the level of the groundwater, however, drainage may not solve the problem alone. In such cases the foundation

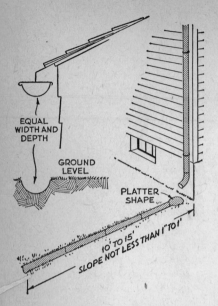

EQUAL WIDTH AND DEPTH

GROUND LEVEL

PLATTER SHAPE

10' TO 15'
SLOPE NOT LESS THAN 1" TO 1'

Fig. 4. Where downspouts are not connected to an outlet, it is advisable to place a spatter board or splash block, or a gutter of good size, at the outlet to divert roof water away from the wall.

walls and floors must be waterproofed. In new construction this can be done by literally wrapping the entire foundation in a membrane waterproofing paper so that the water will be unable to find any openings. In old homes, or newly completed ones with a water problem, the walls and floors must be treated in such a way as to make them completely watertight. Both of these methods, however, are almost always used in combination with drainage.

Draining Roof Water

Homes with cellars should be provided with eaves, troughs (gutters), and downspouts (conductors or leaders). Otherwise the rain water or snow will run off the roof and fall on the surface outside the foundation wall. It then collects in the ground next to the foundation and looks for weak points in the masonry, or openings between floors and walls. The eaves, troughs and downspouts provide a means of controlling this water and draining it away from the foundation wall. If the ground has a natural slope, roof water drained down in this manner will be inclined to run away from the side of the building. However, if the land is flat, some means of preventing the water from collecting outside the foundation wall must be provided. The downspouts should be connected to a drain emptying into a storm sewer, dry well, open water course or other suitable outlet. Many communities, however, prohibit the draining of surface water into sanitary sewers. Where downspouts are not connected to an outlet, therefore, it is advisable to place a spatter board or splash block, or a gutter of good size, at the outlet to divert the roof water away from the wall, (Fig. 4).

This can be accomplished by means of an elbow or shoe. Place it at the bottom of each conductor pipe so that roof water may be drained into the concrete splash gutter. This should be constructed so that it will lead the water at least 10 or 15 feet away from the building wall. The depression or gutter should be of the same width and depth as the eaves gutter being handled, or an equivalent cross-section which may be shallower and wider. The edges of the splash gutter are made level with the surrounding ground. The slope, away from the building, should be not less than 1 inch per foot of length. Splash gutters may be of brickwork, but a V-shaped wooden trough will do. Some are U-shaped and made of wood, brick or stone. A few lengths of half-round vitrified gutter pipe may also be used. To catch all the discharge from a downspout the upper end of the gutter should be widened and shaped like a platter.

Roof water can often be piped underground to a suitable drain, abandoned well, dry well or surface outlet. The latter should be situated 15 or more feet away from the building. Cement the downspout into a piece of cast iron pipe about 2 feet above the ground. Then extend it to a quarter-turn elbow set below frost depth. Complete the line to the well outlet using ordinary drain tile or sewer pipe with cemented joints. An easy way of removing obstructions in the elbow or drain is to set a Y cleanout in the cast iron riser. A branch with a removable plug just above the ground surface can also be used. This plug should be removed about once a year to make sure that no obstruction is forming. To clean it, merely insert a flexible metal snake. This is a long flexible rod with a conical metal end which is used to push out dirt and debris. It's a good idea to have this rod as part of your maintenance equipment.

In some cities rain water may be discharged into the same sewer that carries sewage. In still others, it may be discharged into a separate storm sewer; but in many cities, especially in rural areas, some other means of disposing of water must be used. The usual method is to run water into structures called dry wells.

Dry Wells

The dry well should be made large enough so that it can handle the number of downspouts connected to it. Its effectiveness, however, will depend upon the natural drainage of the ground at the location where the well is dug. Otherwise, the dry well will only be a temporary measure. The hole will fill up, overflow, and cause water to back up in the drain pipes.

Locate a dry well at least 8 or 12 feet away from the house. Line it with brick or cesspool block, laid up with cement. This makes it possible for water to seep in through the sides as well as at the bottom. The well should be covered with a slab of concrete or a cesspool cover. Dig the hole to a depth a little below the house footing. Make it deep enough to allow for at least 12 inches of soil above the well cover. The well should be deeper and wider if the soil is of fine sand, sandy loam, clay or loam. If the downspout measures 3 inches in diameter, the well should be 3 feet in diameter and 3½ feet in depth if situated in coarse sand or gravel soil. In fine sand or sandy loam, where the size of the downspout is still only 3 inches in diameter, the well should then have a width of 6 feet and a depth of 5

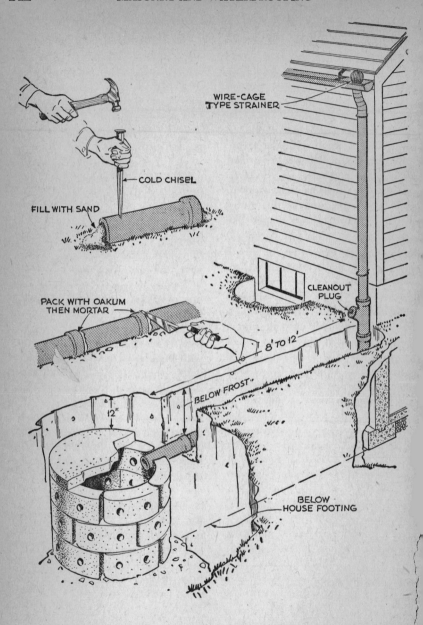

Fig. 5. In constructing a dry well, lay up the concrete blocks in tongue and groove style to give the well a cylindrical shape.

feet. As the diameter of the down-spout increases the depth of the well should be increased.

Lay up the concrete blocks in tongue and grove style to give the well a cylindrical shape, (Fig. 5). Fill the space outside of the well with sand. Use terra-cotta drain tiles to carry water from the downspout. Lay them down at an angle of about one inch in each foot so the water will flow smoothly. If it's necessary to cut a tile, fill it with sand and cut it with a cold chisel. The sand will keep the tile from cracking. Cement the tile joints using mortar made of one part cement to three parts of fine sand. Pack oakum into the bell, or flared end of the tile, before working in the mortar.

Before filling in the earth above the drain, test the dry well by letting water run through it. Low spots are easily corrected. Simply raise the tiles by wedging small stones under both sides. The wire cage type of strainer mentioned previously, should be installed at the top of the down-pout to catch leaves and prevent hem from clogging the drainage system. If there is a great deal of snow and ice, be sure that it does not interfere with the flow of water into the well. Large chunks of ice or snow which form inside the dry well should be melted so that the well will not fill up and force the water to back up in the pipes. Dry wells should be inspected once a year at lease, and more often if there have been unusually severe snow storms.

A temporary dry well can be made from an ordinary barrel or drum,

(Fig. 6). Remove the top and bottom and sink the barrel into the ground about six feet. Fill with gravel and coat with asphalt. Then connect the drain. Put on a wire mesh or other cover and shovel back the topsoil. This kind of well, however, will only give satisfactory performance for a limited time. After a while it inevitably becomes clogged up with leaves and other debris and is difficult to maintain. It is sometimes just as easy to make a brand new well as to clean out an old one.

Surface Drainage

Dampness and leakage in the basement are often due to the fact that the ground around the house is

REMOVE TOP AND BOTTOM, FILL WITH GRAVEL

WIRE MESH

6'

COAT WITH ASPHALT

Fig. 6. A temporary dry well can be made from an ordinary barrel or drum.

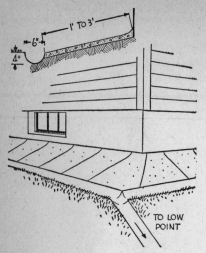

Fig. 7. It is also possible to achieve surface drainage by building a sloping strip around the outside of the house at the juncture of the wall and ground.

flat, or slopes in the direction of the building. This causes water to flow down the sides of the building between the space where the ground and the foundation walls meet. If the rainfall has been particularly severe this water may even penetrate below the foundation floor. It will exert a pressure and leak through any openings or passageways it can find.

Since water moves downward much more quickly than it moves laterally, proper surface drainage is often all that is needed to prevent leakage from occurring in this manner. The idea is to regrade the ground so that as soon as the water strikes it, it will tend to run off away from the building. Simply add soil and build a smooth, sharp, downward slope. Extend it so that it runs

at least 10 feet away from the building. When the grading has been completed it should be seeded with a good lawn grass, raked and rolled. When regrading soil around a home that is set very low in the ground care must be taken with windows. The new grading may run above the bottom of basement windows. In order to maintain the same grade all the way around the house, therefore, it is necessary to build a small concrete parapet or wall around the outside of the window. These may be either curved or rectangular in shape and can be made of concrete, brick or tile. Sometimes a piece of steel or other metallic sheeting is used to shape the concrete wall and also to provide additional protection for the window.

The wells that are formed by these small dams in front of the windows should receive special treatment. Some way of draining the water which may collect in them must be devised. A 4 to 6 foot trench can be dug and a few lengths of tile installed so that the water will be led away from the window well and drained to some outside source, or the window well drainage can be connected with the sub-surface drainage system. When severe rain storms or snow storms occur it is also a good idea to provide a temporary cover for these windows. Covers should be large enough to prevent water from collecting in the well.

It is also possible to achieve surface drainage by building a sloping concrete strip around the outside of the house at the juncture of the wall and ground, (Fig. 7). The pavement may be made of portland cement concrete or bituminous concrete and is usually 1 to 3 feet wide. It sheds water more quickly, but is often objected to because of its appearance. The strips should be rounded up where they join the wall. The water will tend to run off the strip and sink into the ground. If the ground does not slope away from the strip, therefore, it may be desirable to place a trough or gutter about 5 inches along the outside edge of the strip. This gutter is usually made about 6 inches wide and 4 inches deep, and is sloped its entire length so that it will carry water to some low point where it can be discharged.

Filling

After a house has been built the open space between cellar walls and excavation is backfilled. This should be done with the earth that was originally removed. It is common practice, however, for workers to use all the extraneous left-overs they may have lying around for that purpose, so that they do not have to cart it away. They fill this area with pieces of stone, broken bricks, cement bags, bits of wood and mortar, and any other material they could not use in the construction.

When leakage or dampness appears in a basement of a relatively new home it is always a good idea to check this fill. The porous nature of such materials will offer no resistance to water in the ground. Consequently, the water will easily pass through it and seek points at which

it may penetrate through to the basement. Dig down a few feet and examine the material. If porous material has been used it should be cleaned out. Then refill the area, using a layer of gravel at the bottom, a layer of sand above this and, finally, fill to the top with earth which has been packed as tightly as possible. One or two rain storms will tend to pack this earth fill more solidly. Then top soil may be added to complete the job. If the space is not too wide, concrete may be used.

Sub-Surface Drainage

Sometimes adequate surface drainage is not possible. Shrubbery or trees close to the house may make it undesirable to regrade or build a concrete strip. Then, too, standing water may appear regularly in the basement, indicating that the cellar floor is below the level of the ground water for long periods. If so, subsurface drainage is necessary. In addition, where roof water cannot be properly drained off away from the foundation walls by means of ground drainage, a connection can be made from the downspouts down to the sub-surface drainage system.

Footing drains may be installed either on the outside or inside of the footing. In either case, however, a trench and drain is necessary to carry the water away after it has been collected. In order to install an outside footing drain you must excavate down to the footing all around the house. To install an inside footing drain it is necessary to cut through the basement floor around

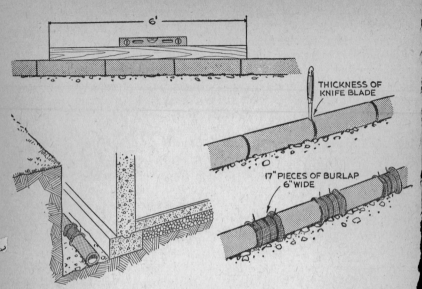

THICKNESS OF
KNIFE BLADE

17" PIECES OF BURLAP
6" WIDE

Fig. 8. To build an outside footing drain, use tile drain measuring about 4 inches in diameter.

the cellar wall. Whether it is preferable to construct the drain on the outside or on the inside of the footing depends on many things.

If the cellar has a lot of equipment, a finished tile floor, or some expensive carpentry which would have to be removed or destroyed in order to cut through the floor, it would probably be more practical and economical to dig a trench around the outside of the foundation. On the other hand, it is a costly and difficult job to excavate a trench all around the foundation walls. Moreover, it is extremely difficult to work in such narrow confines. Generally, therefore, the inside footing drain is more convenient and satisfactory.

If the house is on a hillside, it may only be necessary to install the drain along the high side, but generally it is better to surround the basement with the drain. The idea is to capture the large quantity of water which is below the ground surface and run it away from the foundation.

To build an outside footing drain, use tile drain measuring about 4 inches in diameter, (Fig. 8). Lay it along the bottom of the wall or footing course, taking care not to undermine the footing. Good concrete pipe, well-burned drain tile, or ordinary sewer pipe may be used. A very slight slope should be provided, about 1 inch to every foot. This requires considerable care to make sure that all tile tilts in the direction of the flow of the water. A simple method of maintaining the slope is to make a 6-ft. board 3/20's of an inch narrower at one end than at the other. Place this board edgewise on the tile and mount a level on top of it. The narrower end of the board is, of course, upstream. When the top of the board is level the bottom edge will be sloping down at the rate of 1 foot in every 400 feet. Another method is to grade pairs of stakes on each side of the trench. Then stretch a cord across so that it touches the tops of all of them. The exact depth of the inside of each pipe is measured from the string by a stick having a right angle foot at the bottom.

In very porous soils the tile can be placed directly on the bottom of the trench. In moderately porous soils, however, it is better to make the trench wide enough so that the tile can be surrounded with sand. The sand not only helps to collect water, but also hinders the flow of silt from the soil to the tile line. In clay soils the tile should be surrounded with coarse gravel instead of sand.

The joints should be kept open about the thickness of a knife's blade. Measures must also be taken to keep out loose dirt. Burlap, linen or some other porous fabric 6 inches wide and about 17 inches long should be tied or wired around each joint. Test the system by introducing water at various points. If the pitch is correct the water will drain away from the house. If it is not, it may settle at some low point in the system. Then the slope can be adjusted by wedging stones beneath it. An inexpensive sub-surface drainage method is to fill the bottom of the trench with gravel or broken stone to a depth of about a foot. Then cover this gravel

with a strip of roofing paper to prevent dirt and silt from filling up the spaces between the gravel. If the trench has been properly dug and graded this will provide good drainage without the installation of drain tile. Backfill should then be added on top of the paper.

An extensive drainage system will contain two kinds of lines: those which collect the water and are called laterals, and those which carry away the water poured into them by the laterals. The lines into which laterals drain are made of bell-and-spigot tile. Joints are made by placing a spigot in a bell with the bell end downgrade. The spigot end is then wrapped with a piece of small rope so as to keep it centered in the bell.

The lines must be placed so that they will carry off the water, but otherwise it is not necessary to bury them more than 12 or 15 inches even in regions with cold winters. Soil of this depth will give enough protection to the tile against damage by vehicles which might pass over the lines. Possible frost damage can also be ignored, because if the lines are laid so that their slope is uniform and the outlet is open, they will never be full of water when frost strikes them. A steep slope does no harm, but a slope as gradual as 1 inch in 50 feet is sufficient.

The excavation should be refilled very carefully. Sometimes two operations produce better results. In the first, the trench is filled approximately half full with soil from which all large stones and roots have been picked out. This fill is, of course, placed on top of the sand or gravel, which should range from ¼ to 1 inch in size, with the finer pieces being placed over and around the pipe to give good bedding and protection. To prevent loose dirt from washing down into the stone or cinders, the top should be covered with old bagging, burlap, hay, straw, cornstalks, sods with grass-side down, or fine brush. This should be allowed to settle for a week or longer. Then the remainder of the trench should be filled up to the finished grade. Cover with a foot of top soil. Then grade, seed and tamp it lightly as it is being placed.

A drain and belt of coarse material thus placed around a basement

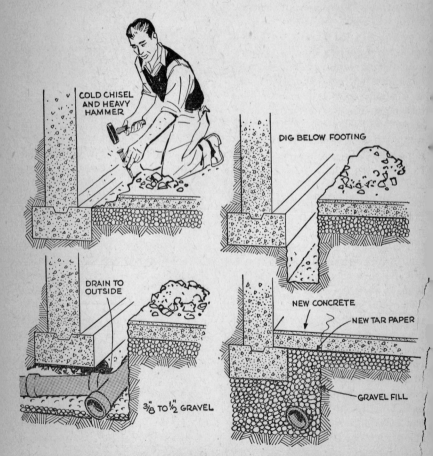

Fig. 9. Usually when the house is already built, it is more convenient and economical to install the drain tile on the inside.

floor will help intercept moisture coming from the soil in the form of capillarity.

The drain tile should be conducted away from the building to a storm sewer or to low ground where it can discharge. It should not be piped into a nearby stream or body of water unless the high point of the stream or body of water is well below the level of the outlet from the drain. Otherwise a heavy rainfall or snow storm will cause the stream to overflow its banks and the water will back up in the drain tile. Where a suitable outlet is not readily available, it may be necessary to connect the drain tile to a sump pit or cistern inside the basement. The pump, automatically controlled, will then remove the water when it reaches a pre-determined level, even though the flow from the drains may be intermittent and varied.

Usually when the house is already built it is more convenient and economical to install the drain tile on the inside, (Fig. 9). To do this, cut out the basement floor along the footing. Be sure enough of an opening is made so that you can install a 4-inch drain pipe. To determine the necessary width of the opening take a section of the drain pipe and mark out on the surface of the floor, with chalk, a line to indicate how much of the floor is to be removed. This can then be cut out with a cold chisel and a sledge or heavy hammer. It can even be cut with a pick. After the section has been removed, excavate the earth under the floor to a depth that will permit the pipe to

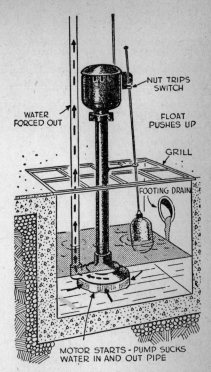

Fig. 10. When outside drainage is not practical, it is advisable to purchase and install a suitable sump pump.

rest below the bottom of the footing. It will also be necessary to remove enough earth under the footing so that the connection between the drain pipe on the inside, and the pipes to be used to carry the water away, can be made. The drain should have open permeable joints and pass through, or under, the footing to an outlet that is open at all times. It should be laid in ⅜ to ½ inch gravel. If necessary to drain deeper than the foundation, the drain may be placed 4 or 5 feet away from the foundation, to avoid undermining it. It is sometimes desirable to lay one or two branch drains to tap springs within a cellar. Then fill up the drainage to the level of the under side of the floor. Place a strip of roofing paper over the gravel so that the concrete will not be able to run in between it. The floor should then be installed over the paper with a mixture of one part portland cement, two parts clean sand and four parts broken stone or gravel. This concrete should be brought up to the level of the top of the floor. It should then be floated and trowelled to the level of the old floor. The inside drain can then be connected with an outlet for disposing of the water collected by the drain.

Sump Pumps

If it is impractical to carry the water away from the footing drain to some low point outside of the building, a sump pump should be installed inside the basement, (Fig. 10).

These pumps are constructed with electrical motors and float switches. When water reaches a pre-determined height the float automatically closes the switch and starts the motor and pump. The water in the pit is then pumped up to the ground level where it may be run off. After the water has been pumped out of the pit to a pre-determined lower level, the float opens the switch and automatically stops the motor and pump.

The size and type of pump required is determined by the amount of water, measured in gallons, to be pumped per minute, and the height to which that water is to be raised

before it is discharged. Where a great deal of leakage has occurred in the basement, it is a good idea to keep track of the number of pailfuls or shovelfuls removed. In this way, the amount of water that must be removed by a sump pump can be estimated.

Sump Pits

Since various types and sizes of sump pumps are available, it is a good idea first to pick out the type desired, and secondly to obtain the dimensions from the manufacturer so that you will know what size pump pit is needed to accommodate that particular unit. The pit should be large enough to hold the body of water which will be removed by the pump in about half a minute. A pit that is too small will cause the automatic switch to start and stop the motor more times each hour and will therefore create unnecessary wear and strain.

A pit of larger capacity will keep the pump operating for a longer period and will start and stop less frequently each hour. The pit should be made of concrete, with openings for the footing drain to discharge its water. The top of the pit should be level with the basement floor. The bottom should be at the necessary depth to hold the amount of water pre-determined necessary for efficient and economical service of the pump and automatic switch. Drainage usually reaches the pit slowly and intermittently, depending on soil conditions and rainfall. Very effective sump pits may be constructed with a section of 36-inch sewer pipe installed vertically through the floor. Holes will have to be drilled through the pipe, however, to permit the footing drain to empty into this sewer pipe sump.

Another method that is sometimes effectively used for the construction of a sump pit is to place a large earthen crock through the basement floor so that the top of the crock is level with the floor, (Fig. 11). Holes are cut through the sides of the crock to permit the footing drain to empty into the sump.

Cellar Drainers

If a large amount of water is discovered in the basement the easiest way to remove it is to use some type of cellar drainer, *(See Fig. 3B, Ch. 6.)* This is a small, simple, compact appliance. It is about the size of a nozzle on an ordinary garden hose. The inlet and outlet ends are threaded and perforations encircle the drainer about halfway from each end. It operates on the ejector principle. One end must be attached to a supply of water under pressure, and the other end attached to a pipe, or hose, through which the water is discharged at ground level.

PREVENTING LEAKAGE

Leakage is caused by water under pressure. This is important to bear in mind in order to properly understand waterproofing methods. To prevent leakage from occurring in a basement, therefore, the water must

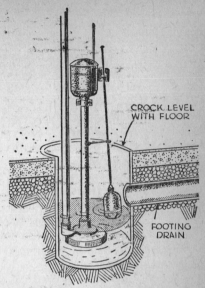

CROCK LEVEL WITH FLOOR

FOOTING DRAIN

Fig. 11. Another method effectively used for the construction of a sump pit is to place a large earthen crock through the basement floor so that the top of the crock is level with the floor.

either be diverted away from the foundation by some form of drainage previously described, or the walls and floor of the foundation must be treated to withstand the pressure.

Satisfactory waterproofing involves treatment of all exposed surfaces. This is necessary because the water in the ground is always active. If you waterproof one side of a wall, for example, leakage may occur through the floor or through another side. In other words, one wall which has been waterproofed will simply force the water to seek some other place where it can enter the foundation. Unless the pressure is very small, therefore, partial waterproofing will never be completely satisfactory.

For this reason, complete waterproofing always requires application or treatment of both the floor and walls of the foundation. This is usually easier to do, and about one-tenth as costly, when the home is being built. A membrane waterproofing system, for example, cannot be applied properly after construction has been completed. The idea of the membrane treatment involves wrapping the entire foundation in heavy, waterproof paper. It is therefore virtually impossible to put in a membrane system once the building has been completed.

The usual method of waterproofing a foundation, which involves integrating a waterproofing compound in the concrete mixture, is also impossible to use once the building has been constructed. A new concrete floor can be waterproofed and put down in the basement to prevent leakage through the floor, but this should not be considered as full protection for the entire basement against penetration by water under pressure. The water that has been coming through the basement floor may then merely be diverted against the walls. Concrete foundation walls, of course, cannot be easily replaced.

Forms of integral waterproofing may be used, however, to adequately waterproof the basement after construction has been completed. It should be emphasized again, however, that the basement will be completely secure from the threat of leakage only if *all* walls and the floor are properly waterproofed. Merely plugging the holes or cracks in a wall where leakage has appeared will not assure dryness in the basement. At best, such methods will only temporarily alleviate the condition. Patching and re-pointing may have to be undertaken at regular intervals in order to prevent water under pressure from getting through at new points.

Inside or Outside Waterproofing

Once a house has been built it is always easier and more effective to waterproof from the inside. Outside waterproofing requires an excavation all around the foundation and down to the footing. This is hard work if it is done by the homeowner himself and expensive if it is not. In addition, it is extremely difficult to work properly in a narrow trench. It will be easier to apply the waterproofing at the top of the foundation walls than near the bottom. Yet it is at the bottom where the danger is greatest. The water pressure around footings

Fig. 12. Once a house has been built it is easier to waterproof from the inside, for a man cramped in a small trench cannot do as good a job on the lower portions.

is stronger and more likely to cause leakage than farther up the foundation wall.

A man cramped in a small trench, (Fig. 12), cannot be expected to do as good a job on the lower portions. It is also natural that outside labor will be less concerned about workmanship on an outside waterproofing job, because after they are through their work is covered over and hidden. On the inside, however, the workmanship is always open for inspection and poor craftsmanship is easy to detect.

Waterproofing from the inside is easier because there is plenty of room to move around and do an equally good job both on lower and upper portions of the walls. Be sure to use an integral waterproofing material, however, which will form a mixture that adheres properly to the surface of the wall. Some integral waterproofing compounds of the water repellent type, for example, are difficult to handle and require expert manipulation in order to obtain a good bond or make the mixture adhere properly to the surface of the wall.

Where brickwork is a part of the architectural design of the basement, outside waterproofing will be necessary, because any inside waterproofing would cover the brick. When a membrane waterproofing was used during construction of the building, outside repair work may also be necessary. Leakage may be due to a tear in the membrane. The only way this can be corrected is to dig a trench around the outside foundation walls and down to the footings. Then the tear will have to be patched.

The following text concerns ways and means of preventing water under pressure from making cellars wet and damp. These are techniques which can be used if problems arise in old homes or in new ones, shortly after construction. Planning ways and means of assuring a dry basement during initial construction, however, is a wise preventive measure.

INSIDE WATERPROOFING

When leakage appears in a basement which was waterproofed during construction, several factors may be to blame. Faulty workmanship, poor materials, ineffective waterproofing, building settlement and new conditions, such as remodeling and new plumbing, may be responsible. If the hydrostatic pressure is not too great the leaks may be stopped by merely patching or plugging the spots where they appear. A more serious situation, however, may require laying a new floor or applying fresh waterproofing to a wall. Where there are definite indications that proper waterproofing was included in the original construction, these corrective measures may be undertaken. However, where no waterproofing system was used, or evidence of it has completely disappeared, a complete waterproofing job for the entire basement is necessary. In any case, all of this work is easier and more effective when it is performed from the inside.

Plugging Leaks

When a small portion of a wall becomes sieve-like or honeycombed, the entire piece should be removed, (Fig. 13). Using a cold chisel and hammer, cut the section away to the boundaries of the dense, solid concrete. Then clean the spot that has been cut out and wet it thoroughly. While the surface is still wet, scrub it with a grout composed of one part portland cement, one part fine sand, and water. Mix until it has the consistency of thick cream. Apply it with a stiff fiber brush, using a rotary motion. While the grout is still wet, patch the wall opening with new concrete.

Cracks are repaired as follows: Cut away the concrete on each side of the crack to a depth and total width of 1 or 2 inches. Use hammer and chisel for this purpose also. First clean the cut surfaces, wet them, and seal the crack at the base of the opening by scrubbing in a cement grout. This should be done before the opening is filled. While the grout is still wet, fill the opening with a cement mortar containing one part portland cement to two parts of sand mixed with a waterproofing compound.

The method and materials used to plug leaks depends on the size and shape of the crack. Cracks at construction joints, such as those between the basement walls and floor, may be relatively wide and straight in direction. They are effectively sealed with oakum. The oakum must be rammed in so that its surface is slightly below the base of the cut in the concrete. The cut surface is then

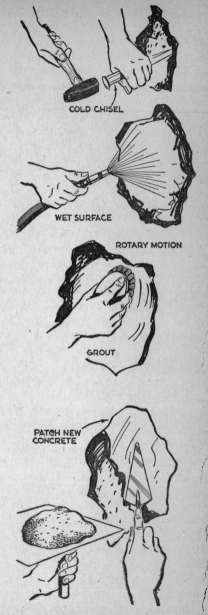

COLD CHISEL

WET SURFACE

ROTARY MOTION

GROUT

PATCH NEW CONCRETE

Fig. 13. Technique for repairing a portion of honeycombed wall.

scrubbed while still damp, with a cement grout. Cement mortar is used to fill the opening.

A fillet of the mortar may be placed at cracks situated at the junction of the wall and floor. It may be formed by finishing its surface with a round bottle. Rub the bottle back and forth into the soft mortar and along the line of the joint between the wall and floor, *(See Fig. 3B, Ch. 6)*. This leaves a uniform, quarter round fillet or cove, and is easier to keep clean than a sharp intersection between wall and floor.

To stop an actual flow of water, a mixture consisting of one part portland cement and one part sand, and having the consistency of putty, can be pressed into the opening and held there by means of a form or a small board until it is sufficiently hardened to stay in place.

Bleeding the Wall

If water is seeping rapidly through a sizeable area of a basement wall it may be difficult to repair the leaks as described above. This occurs when the water has a number of places it can get through. As soon as one hole is plugged, the water leaks through another one. Steps must be taken to localize the flow so that the water will be drawn through only one hole. Then the rest of the leaky section can be sealed up with cement mortar. Sometimes this pressure can be relieved by pumping the water away from the outside of the foundation wall, but when this is not possible, a pipe inserted through a hole on the inside wall will do the job. The hole

is sometimes referred to as a "weep hole."

To construct a "weep hole," use a hammer and a star drill, (Fig. 14). Cut a hole through the wall near the floor, or below the porous section giving trouble. The water will then seek the point of least resistance in the wall. It will run through the hole and into the basement. Take an ordinary piece of pipe and insert it into the hole. Make sure that it is long enough to reach the exterior side of the wall. It should also extend far enough inside the cellar so that water running through it may be collected in buckets for removal, or it may be attached to a piece of hosing which will carry the water away to some drainage point. If large quantities of water come through the pipe, a sump pump or cellar drainer should be used to remove the water from the basement floor.

If the water cannot be satisfactorily localized through one pipe, others should be inserted in the same manner. Once the water flow has been relegated to the pipes, the entire section should be treated with cement mortar. The water pressure must be kept away from the wall long enough to permit the mortar to harden and set. This may be a matter of two or three days.

After the porous section has been made watertight, the pipe should be removed and the hole plugged with cement mortar. If you wish to leave the pipe in the wall, the room end should be threaded so a cap can be screwed on when it's time to shut off the water. Be sure that the points

STAR DRILL

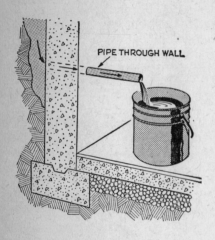

PIPE THROUGH WALL

Fig. 14. To construct a "weep hole," use a hammer and a star drill.

where the pipe enters the wall are tightly sealed.

Openings in Concrete Floors

Concrete floors that are badly cracked can be repaired with a 1-inch topping of cement mortar comprised of one part portland cement to two parts sand. (*See Chapter 1 for*

details on preparation of surface and application.)

Sometimes a new floor can be laid. The thickness will depend on the amount of hydrostatic pressure pushing up against it and the availability of sub-surface drainage. If sub-surface drainage is not provided and hydrostatic pressure is great, a concrete floor of considerable thickness is necessary. Ordinary concrete will withstand pressure equal to a head of water 2¼ times the thickness of the concrete. A 6-inch floor, for example, will hold out the pressure created by water standing 9 inches above the floor line, or 15 inches above the bottom of the floor.

When a floor cannot be under-drained and is subjected to strong hydrostatic pressure it may be necessary to lay a basement floor of reinforced concrete. This requires a design of steel and concrete to be worked out by a structural engineer.

If the hydrostatic pressure is not too strong, and sub-surface drainage is installed, a new basement floor between 2 to 4 inches thick will usually be satisfactory.

Before laying a new concrete floor, be sure that it will not interfere with some piece of equipment or device installed in the basement. A new floor will reduce the height of the room. If this is not advisable, it will be necessary to repair the old concrete floor. Where sub-surface drainage cannot be installed and hydrostatic pressure is powerful, it may be best to employ an engineer to determine the kind of floor needed to assure protection against leakage.

Preparing Surfaces

Before any application is put on a wall, whether it be mortar, paint, or a wash of some sort, be sure the surface upon which the application is to be made is thoroughly clean and free of oils, grease, paint or whitewash. Any sharp tool such as a scraper or a wire brush can be used to remove dry foreign matter on the surface, *(See Fig. 9, Ch. 7).* If however, the foreign matter has penetrated into the surface as oil stains or grease, use a detergent to remove it. The surface should then be thoroughly hosed down with clean water so that none of the detergent, acid, or other material will be left in the masonry wall.

If the surface which is to be treated consists of any type of masonry mortar previously applied on the wall such as a cement rendering or stucco, be sure that the existing coating is tight on the wall. This can be determined by gently tapping the surface with a hammer. Hollow sections will sound entirely different from the solid masonry. All hollow loose parts should be cut out or cut away and replaced before any surface application of waterproofing or dampproofing is applied.

Cement-mortar Coatings

When a complete waterproofing job is needed in the basement of an old house, coating the floor and walls, on the inside, with cement-mortar is most effective. A cement-mortar coating can also be used on a single wall, or on the floor, if other basement surfaces were properly waterproofed when the cellar was built. Otherwise, application of a cement-mortar coating to a single surface will merely divert the leakage to another part of the basement.

The best time of year to apply a cement-mortar coating is during a dry spell when the basement walls or floor show little free water. First, remove everything from the basement walls and floor so that every inch of wall space may be covered with mortar. This includes not only loose furniture or garden equipment, but also water or hot air pipes, gas or electric meters, the boiler and the furnace, in fact, anything that might interfere with complete accessibility to walls and floor. This is essential. If any area is left uncovered, it will be the

Fig. 15. Proper preparation and moistening of all surfaces is essential in cement-mortar waterproofing. Just before applying the plaster, give the moist surface a brush coat of neat portland cement grout.

weak link through which water will enter the basement.

Proper preparation of all surfaces is also essential to the success of the cement-mortar waterproofing. Remove any whitewash or paint with a cold chisel and hammer. Get right down to virgin masonry be it brick, tile, cement or cinder block. Use a wire brush to roughen the surface of the floor or wall slightly so that the mortar will stick. It should be kept wet by drenching with clean water for several hours prior to the application of the plaster. A dry surface will absorb moisture from the plaster and prevent proper setting and bonding.

Just before applying the plaster, give the moist surface a brush coat of neat portland cement grout, (Fig. 15). Then, while this slush coat is still wet, apply a cement-mortar made of one part portland cement and two parts of clean sand mixed with a liquid, powder or paste waterproofing compound, according to the instructions of the manufacturer. Each plaster coat should then be applied before the coat beneath it sets. This makes it easier to form a good bond. Scratch each undercoat lightly or score it with a saw tooth paddle (Fig. 16), a piece of metal lath, or a sharp stick, in checkerboard-like fashion, to improve the mechanical bond with the next coat. All coats, except the final one, should be well worked with wooden float to make the surface slightly granular. The last coat should, however, be floated carefully to leave a straight surface. A smooth trowelled surface is more

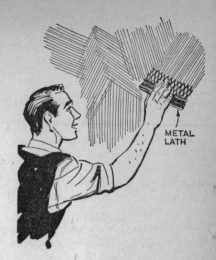

Fig. 16. When applying cement-mortar waterproofing coatings, scratch each undercoat lightly or score it with a sawtooth paddle.

likely to sweat than a rough, floated one.

Apply at least two coats of cement-mortar to the walls to give a total thickness of not less than ⅝ of an inch. The floor topping should be not less than one inch thick. Lay each coat in one operation on wall and floor. Cove all corners. Since joints, angles, and corners are the weak places, try to make as few of these as possible. Joints should be made on the wall, or on the floor, a foot or more from an angle or corner.

If the floor is to be plastered first and the walls must wait, the plastering should be carried up the walls about a foot, leaving a rough bevelled edge. This is later wet, brush coated with grout, and bonded with the wall plaster. Wall plastering should be started by making a rough vertical bevelled edge on the flat surface, as it is difficult to make a tight closure at a corner. The plastering should be completed with as few vertical joints as possible.

If the walls are done first, the plastering should be carried out on the floor about a foot, leaving a rough bevelled edge to be grouted and bonded with the floor plaster, (Fig 17). The latter method (walls first) is usually more convenient, but the first method (floor first) is more likely to give a watertight job because the joint work is at a higher level. If the walls must be done first, however, a good procedure is to place boards along the bottom of the wall and apply the plaster down to the edge of the boards, (Fig. 18). When the plaster sets, remove the boards and install the floor with fillets

PLASTER WALL FIRST

OLD FLOOR

Fig. 17. If the walls are done first in cement-mortar waterproofing, the plastering should be carried out on the floor about a foot, leaving a rough, bevelled edge to be grouted and bonded with the floor plaster.

which can be joined to the bottom of the wall plaster.

Plaster dries quickly and may crack. Just as soon as it is sufficiently hard so that the cement will not be washed away, it should be drenched and kept continuously wet or flooded for at least a week. Properly applied, the cement-mortar coating will be most effective in preventing leakage. When a building settles, however, cracks may appear and disrupt the mortar waterproofing. These may be repaired in the manner described under *Plugging Leaks,* above.

Cement-Grout Coatings

Where leaks in masonry walls are relatively small the entire wall can be coated with a cement grout made and applied as described under*Plugging Leaks.* A liquid waterproofing compound added to the grout will, however, increase its ability to resist leakage. The grout should have the consistency of thick cream.

Cement Coatings Containing Powdered Iron

Treatments containing powdered iron may also be used to waterproof the basement from the inside. They usually consist of powdered iron and an oxidizing agent mixed either with or without the addition of portland cement. Use a brush or chipping hammer to roughen surfaces to a depth of $\frac{1}{8}$ to $\frac{1}{4}$ of an inch before applying an iron compound. Hack or chip the wall to remove the entire face. Chemical washes are usually not sufficient to roughen the surface for application of the iron method. Three to five coats should be used, depending on the quantity of water and leakage conditions. Use a stiff bristle brush for the first coat and a soft brush for subsequent coats. A surface treated with the iron oxidation method should be finished with a brush coat of neat cement. To accelerate oxidation, dampen the wall with a water spray, (Fig. 19). An insecticide spray gun can be used. In confined spaces air circulation may be secured by means of a fan. Windows should also be kept open during all applications. Iron oxidation mixtures applied to the floor require a protective coating. A one-inch topping, made of one part portland cement and two parts sand, properly bonded, may be used.

Fig. 18. If the walls are done first in cement-mortar waterproofing, a good procedure is to place boards along the bottom of the wall and apply the plaster down to their edges.

OUTSIDE WATERPROOFING

Water proofing treatments applied to the outside surfaces of basements are sometimes necessary. The chief objection, however, to this approach is that a trench must be dug down to the foot of the foundation wall in order to apply the waterproofing. The excavation must be wide enough to work in, and should be extended all the way around the foundation walls.

Repairing Membrane

If a membrane waterproofing system was used to prevent leakage when the cellar was built, subsequent leakage may be due to a tear or hole in the membrane. Dig a trench around the entire foundation and

to the footings. Locate the hole or tear and cover it with a piece of tar paper or felt. Then coat it with hot tar or asphalt. (See Effect of Installations, Ch. 7).

Leakage sometimes occurs because the membrane was not carried high enough when it was originally laid. The water may pass over the top of the membrane paper and come down on the inside. It will then seek weak spots in foundation surfaces and leak through to the interior of the basement. The membrane should be extended so that it goes up to 6 inches above the ground all around the foundation, (Fig. 20). Then seal it at the top with tar.

Bituminous Coatings

When water conditions are not so severe and walls are not subjected

ig. 19. To accelerate oxidation when applying cement coatings containing powdered iron, dampen the wall with a water spray.

o water under pressure, a relatively expensive method of waterproofing e exterior walls is applying a coat-g of bituminous material without bric. These coatings are both cold-plied and hot-applied. The latter re superior, however, because they provide more bitumen per unit area than the cold-applied coatings, even though the latter are easier to handle.

Bituminous coatings are sometimes used when it is necessary to install a drain tile around the outside of the footings, or when some other work being done to the basement requires an excavation.

The exterior walls must first be coated with a cement mortar. Rough walls should be given a grout coat of

cement mortar and allowed to dry before bituminous coatings are applied. Bituminous coatings are used only on the outside of either masonry-unit or monolithic walls. Such coatings on inside walls cause blistering and peeling.

Cold-applied coatings are of heavy-brushing or trowelling consistency. Asphalt or coal-tar pitch is used as the base. They are easier to apply because no heating is necessary. When an asphalt coating is used the wall should first be primed with an asphalt primer. Use a coal-tar or creosote primer with coal-tar coatings. Bituminous coatings may also be applied to cement-mortar coats.

Before applying hot coatings make walls smooth and dry, (Fig. 21). An asphalt primer should be used for hot coal-tar pitch. (*Method for heating is described in the next chapter under Membrane Waterproofing.*) Use a roofer's mop to mop on hot-applied coatings. Spread the coating to a thickness of at least ⅛ of an inch in one or more applications. Bituminous coatings, hot or cold, should extend from 6 inches above the ground line down over the top of the footing. The second coat should be applied with brush strokes at right angles to the strokes of the first coat, (Fig. 22).

Commercial bituminous mortars are also available. These plastic cements are applied with a plasterer's trowel. They are usually comprised of asphalt or some other bituminous material combined with asbestos fiber, mineral filler, and suitable volatile solvents. The cement, ready for use, comes in containers holding from 30 to 500 or more pounds. It should be spread smoothly and evenly without drawing or pulling. A ⅛ inch coating, requiring approximately 80 pounds for 100 square feet, is usually applied to the outside of cellar walls, and a ¼ inch coat is laid on cellar floors. The trench around the foundation may be refilled after the plaster has been allowed to dry at least 24 to 48 hours. Care must be taken not to injure it. Floor plaster should be given a heavy protective covering of portland-cement mortar or concrete.

Repairing Cement-mortar Coatings

If the basement was waterproofed by means of a cement-mortar coating on outside foundations walls when the house was constructed, repairs to the waterproofing will also have to be made on the outside. Cracks in the walls are frequently caused when a building settles. The movement also severs the cement-mortar waterproofing. The source of the water penetration will first have to be discovered and then repaired.

Cracks in outside monolithic concrete walls may be sealed by cutting a groove about 1 inch deep and 1 inch wide. The edges of the cut should first be scrubbed into the groove. Then pack a cement-mortar of stiff consistency into the opening. Because the expense and inconvenience associated with digging a trench is often considerable, when an outside cement-mortar coating is found to be faulty, outside repairs are frequently disregarded in favor

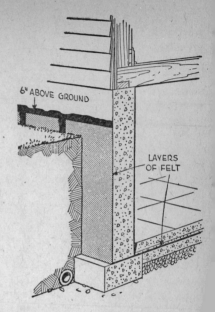

6" ABOVE GROUND

LAYERS OF FELT

Fig. 20. When repairing membrane waterproofing, the membrane should be extended so that it goes up to 6 inches above the ground all around the foundation.

of a new cement-mortar coating applied to inside surfaces.

SEEPAGE AND CAPILLARITY

Seepage is frequently confused and used interchangeably with leakage and capillarity. Actually, it may be used with both leakage and capillarity. When applied with leakage, it implies the movement of water through a surface by means of pressure. This pressure may be hydrostatic, or it may be direct pressure from rain or pipes. It is usually not very great.

Seepage due to hydrostatic pressure may be prevented by dampproofing as well as waterproofing methods. It occurs only when a very mild form of hydrostatic pressure is present. Dampproofing methods are therefore adequate as a remedy. Seepage in the basement may occur when water overflows a tub or basin in the bathroom or kitchen above, finds its way through an opening, and drips down into the cellar, (Fig. 23). It also takes place when water seeps in through tiny holes or cracks in windows, doors or even basement masonry above the surface of the ground.

Sometimes seepage produced by hydrostatic pressure will gather around the outside of foundation surfaces and will be drawn into the interior by means of capillarity. In other words, seepage occurs as a mild form of leakage under hydrostatic pressure and also in combination with capillarity.

Fig. 21. Before applying hot bituminous coatings make the walls smooth and dry.

Dampness, as opposed to actual leakage or seepage, may be transmitted through basement surfaces by means of capillary action. This is particularly true when the soil surrounding the walls and floor is especially damp. Often, the amount of this moisture is so small that it is evaporated by the air and the walls and floor appear to be dry. When there is a great deal of humidity or water vapor in the air in the basement, however, evaporation will not be possible and this moisture will then be deposited on the floor or walls. It is often very difficult to tell the difference between condensation and capillarity. When this moisture appears, therefore, it is suggested that a test for condensation be conducted. (See Tests for Water Conditions, Ch. 5).

Capillarity or "wick action" seldom results in any appreciable amount of moisture when it occurs alone. If the basement is being used for living quarters, or the floor and walls are covered with materials impervious to the air, such as oil paints or linoleum, the dampness and moisture brought on by capillarity will be unpleasant and damaging.

A complication may arise when part of the moisture is the result of condensation. In such cases, additional examination of the damp area is necessary. Cover the damp area with a rubber mat, preferably 3 by 3 feet, (Fig. 24). Let it stand for several days and then re-examine it. If the surface of the floor which is covered is still dry, condensation and not capillary transmission is one of

NEXT COAT AT RIGHT
ANGLE TO FIRST

Fig. 22. In applying bituminous coatings, the second coat should be applied with brush strokes at right angles to the strokes used for the first coat.

floor. The best, and most logical means of dampproofing to prevent seepage, therefore, is to seal up the pores using a dampproofer which integrates with the surface application and thereby prevents water from seeping through. This can be done by applying any one of a number of commercially available products. Most of them are cement-base preparations that you simply mix with water. If you pick a kind that comes in a variety of pastel colors, you can

the causes of dampness. If the area under the mat has become damp and remains damp after surrounding areas have dried, capillarity contributes to the dampness. Moisture due to capillary action enters the basement through tiny holes or pores in the construction. A drainage which minimizes the dampness in the soil surrounding the foundation will reduce the possibility of capillarity. Treatments applied to basement surfaces which seal up the tiny holes and pores will prevent the moisture from reaching the interior of the basement. Methods used to prevent seepage will also provide good protection against capillary transmission of moisture.

Sealing Up the Pores

Seepage or capillarity involves a penetration of water moisture through tiny holes in the walls and

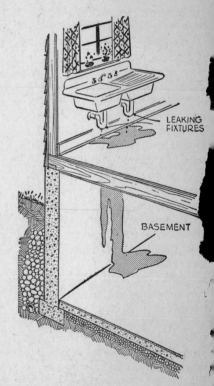

LEAKING
FIXTURES

BASEMENT

Fig. 23. Seepage in the basement may occur when water overflows a basin in the kitchen, finds its way through an opening, and drips down into the basement.

decorate your cellar walls at the same time.

Simply mix portland cement into a solution of water and any liquid waterproofing which reacts chemically with portland cement. The usual proportion is one part of the liquid waterproofing with three parts of water. Then stir enough portland cement into the solution to form the consistency of a heavy paint.

Regardless of what dampproofer you choose, however, the preparation of the wall surfaces is very important. Any sort of finish on them — such as calcimine or oil paint — must be removed.

Remove the old finish first. wire brush, paint remover, solve made by dissolving one pound of trisodium phosphate in one quart of warm water, or use a wash composed of 1 part of muriatic acid and 5 to 10 parts of water. Let this wash stand for about a half-hour. Then flush with a hose, or scrub with a wire or stiff bristle brush to wash off the acid, dirt and loose particles. Clean out and enlarge holes and cracks with a cold chisel and hammer. Undercut sides to form a dovetail that will hold the patch firmly in place, (Fig. 25). Then fill with mortar comprised of one part cement, two parts sand and water. If a leak is actually visible a quick-setting patching cement must be used. After patches set, wet the wall down with fine spray from a hose. Finally, mix dampproofer according to manufacturer's instructions, and scrub it into the wall with a stiff-bristled brush.

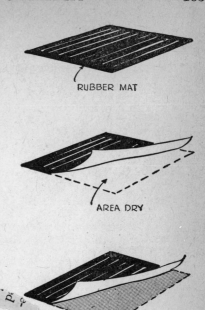

RUBBER MAT

AREA DRY

AREA DAMP

Fig. 24. To determine whether moisture is the result of capillarity or condensation, apply the rubber mat test.

In applying the dampproofer, brush the material into the wall so that it fills every pore. Start at the bottom and gradually work up, (Fig. 26). Since this is a messy process, it's best to wear an old hat and gogles or glasses. Two coats of most dampproofers are generally required. Walls should be thoroughly wetted down after the first coat has dried and before the second one is applied. Use the spray from a garden hose again. The drying time, in most cases, varies from about two to four hours. Don't rush it. After the second coat has dried, see if it will brush off. If not, the wall should be wetted down again, and then again, every twelve hours for the next three days. This continual wetting and drying helps to cure the mixture slowly and makes it an integral part of the wall. If, after the second coat has been thoroughly cured and allowed to dry, you see moist spots here and there, some of the larger pores in the wall surfaces have not been completely filled. They should be enlarged with a cold chisel, filled with patching cement, or a 1 to 2 mortar mixture, and re-treated with the dampproofing solution.

Since all cement-base dampproofers are quick-setting preparations,

Fig. 25. Regardless of what dampproofer you choose, the preparation of wall surfaces is very important. Clean out and enlarge holes and cracks with a cold chisel and hammer, and undercut the sides to form a dovetail that will hold the patch firmly in place.

be sure to wash off any drippings and spatters that might mar your basement floor or other surfaces. If you let them stand too long and they harden, you'll have trouble removing them.

The most widely used effective water-repellent admixtures for concrete contain calcium stearate or ammonium stearate as the water-repellent substance. The "waterproofed" portland cements, which are readily available from building supply dealers, contain a uniformly dispersed water repellent such as calcium stearate and may be used conveniently instead of an admixture and an ordinary cement.

Bituminous Dampproofers

Outside foundation walls may be effectively treated to prevent capillarity and given some protection from leakage by various applications of bituminous materials. These are similar in composition and application to those described under *Outside Waterproofing*, above. They include hot application of coal-tar pitch or asphalt, and cold application of prepared bituminous paints, water-gas tar, and coal tar. The latter are obtainable at city gas works or from manufacturers of roofing materials.

Four coats of very thin water-gas tar are brushed or sprayed on the wall. Each 100 square feet of masonry require 2½ gallons. Sufficient time must be allowed between coats so that each may be properly absorbed by the masonry. After the last coat is dry, refined coal tar should be applied at the rate of ½ to 1 gallon er 100 square feet. Then it is thoroughly brushed in and left to dry for 24 to 48 hours.

Bituminous paints are used strictly for dampproofing purposes. They are applied cold, with an ordinary paint brush. At least two coats are required. The primer should be very thin and should be thoroughly brushed into all pores and minute cracks. The paint is usually applied at the rate of 1 to 1½ gallons per 100 square feet, but the quantity will vary with the porosity and roughness of the surface. Apply the second coat within 24 hours after the first, and at the rate of 1 gallon per 100 square feet. Provide a film approximately one-sixty fourth of an inch thick. Earth backfilling may be done 24 hours after the application of the last coat, care being taken not to bruise or scar the paint.

CONDENSATION

Since most of the basement is submerged in the ground, the temperature of the walls and floor is therefore greatly influenced by the ground temperature. This changes slowly and remains approximately constant throughout the year. As a matter of fact, even points only two or three feet below ground surface vary only a few degrees from the annual mean temperature of a locality.

As a result, the basement walls and floor are likely to be cooler than the outdoor air during summer months, the season when condensation usually occurs in the basement. The warm, humid air coming down from

START AT BOTTOM
WORK UP

Fig. 26. In applying the dampproofer, brush the material into the wall so that it fills every pore. Start at the bottom and gradually work up.

the rest of the house or entering through windows from the outside strikes the cold walls or floor of the basement and condenses. Water will also condense when this warm air comes in contact with equipment or furnishings in the basements with cold surfaces. (*Methods of dealing with condensation caused by warm air in contact with cold water pipes are described under Condensation on Pipes in Chapter 5.*)

Condensation caused in this manner will usually result in dampness and leakage which is visible. When the water condition or dampness is not readily identified as condensation, however, tests may be performed (*See Tests for Water Conditions under Chapter 5.*) Condensation may also occur, however, within the masonry, behind inner surfaces, and this will sometimes not show up in tests for condensation. This moisture may later reach the inner surface of the wall by capillarity. If there is little ventilation and no chance for it to evaporate, it will cause dampness on the walls. This latter condition occurs often in corners and behind large objects situated close to the masonry surfaces.

If the basement walls have been made glossy and impervious by an application of paint, the condensation or "sweating" may be very great. It is quite possible that the lower part of cellar walls may drip and shallow pools of water may form on the floor. This condition may also be caused by water seeping in from the outside. It is, therefore, very important to identify the nature of the

condition before undertaking costly waterproofing measures.

The amount of water vapor is increased when clothes are hung up to dry in a basement, (Fig. 27). This will not be so bad during the winter if proper ventilation is used, but during rainy summer weather when indoor drying is necesary it will greatly increase the possibility of condensation in the cellar. The water vapor content in the basement is also affected by the combustion of fuels containing hydrogen, such as gas, kerosene or other fuel oil. Since all types of heaters are frequently installed in the cellar, the products of their combustion will add to the condensation problem. Their fumes may

Fig. 27. The amount of water vapor is increased when clothes are hung up to dry in the basement.

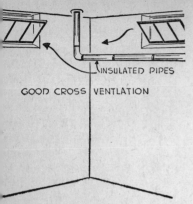

INSULATED PIPES

GOOD CROSS VENTILATION

Fig. 28. When condensation takes place on basement walls or windows during the winter, proper ventilation will generally correct the situation.

owever, be carried outside of the ouse by means of a suitable chimney or vent.

REMEDIES FOR CONDENSATION

Condensation in the basement is only a problem because of its damaging affect on surfaces and furnishings below the ground, but also because it may be drawn up into other parts of the house where it will cause additional discomfort and destruction. It is also possible that a water condition or dampness in the upper floors of the home may be mistakenly attributed to some type of leakage. Dealing with condensation at its source in the basement, therefore, will often do away with dampness in other parts of the house. The following are suggested ways and means of preventing condensa-

tion in the basement. (*A full discussion of condensation and its affect on the entire house is given in Chapter 5.*)

Ventilation

Merely opening windows and doors in order to introduce outside air which will raise the temperature of the surfaces is difficult to do in the basement. In the summertime this warm air may add to the water vapor and humidity in the cellar and increase condensation. It is sometimes better during warm periods to keep as much of the hot outside air as possible from getting into the basement. This will reduce the possibility of condensation.

When condensation takes place on basement walls or windows during the winter, however, proper ventilation, by means of opening and closing doors and windows, will generally correct the situation, (Fig. 28).

Heating

Condensation during the summer is caused by hot outside air striking cold surfaces in the basement. The problem then is to increase the temperature of basement surfaces as much as possible so that it will come close to the temperature of the outside air. Consequently, heat from domestic hot water heaters, operating continuously during the summer, frequently solve condensation problems in basements. In addition, heating devices that are not insulated too effectively are often valuable in reducing condensation in the cellar. A space heater may also be used to raise the temperature of masonry surfaces above the dew point, but ventilation must be provided while the heater is in operation. Waste gases from such heaters should be vented to the outside, (Fig. 29).

While heating may be effective for most of the basement area, it often does not reach remote places such as wall closets, foot lockers, and areas behind drapes. Condensation will consequently still occur in these areas.

Insulation

If the temperature of the inside surfaces of the basement is raised so that it will be close to the temperature of the air, condensation may be prevented. Insulating surfaces with paint, varnish, paper or other thin material, however, is not proper insulation. The insulating material should be cellular glass, or other materials which are vapor barriers, are not absorptive, and are not damaged by moisture. Floor insulation may consist of a thin layer of lightweight aggregate concrete, structural clay tile, hollow concrete units or cellular glass. It should be protected or covered with a wearing surface of cement-mortar, quarry tile, or asphalt tile of suitable thickness.

A layer of cellular glass set in and covered with cement-mortar, or a tier of structural clay tile or hollow concrete units with or without a finished coating may be used for insulating basement walls. Wood should not be used between the insulation and the old wall or floor because it

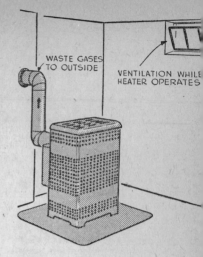

Fig. 29. Heating devices that are not insulated too effectively are often valuable in reducing condensation in the basement. Waste gases from such heaters should be vented to the outside.

may be damaged by moisture in this position.

Condensation is prevented by a vapor barrier placed behind a wood surface. It should run parallel to the furring strips and lap only over solid supports. The idea is to prevent accumulation of free water behind the ornamental panel. The top and bottom furring strips *(for application of a vapor barrier see Vapor Barrier in Chapter 5)*, and those around windows and other openings, should be continuous in order to form a good seal.

Dehumidification

Condensation in the basement can be prevented by removing some of

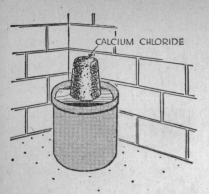

Fig. 30. The chemical type of dehumidifier involves the use of calcium chloride, or some other substance, which has the capacity to absorb moisture from the air.

the moisture from the air. Air-conditioning will bring on an even temperature. This, however, is a costly way of preventing condensation and, unless the basement is used extensively, it is not recommended.

Chemical and mechanical dehumidifiers may also be used. The chemical type involves the use of calcium chloride, or some other substance, which has the capacity to absorb moisture from the air, (Fig. 30). Lithium chloride, silica gel and activated alumina are also suitable materials. Supplies of calcium chloride, trays, and directions for its use can be obtained from building supply dealers. It is relatively inexpensive, costing about 3 cents per pound in 100-pound bags. However, it can be used only once, and must be disposed of when liquid. As is absorbs

moisture from the air it dissolves. This solution must be emptied into drains which must be flushed well as the solution is highly corrosive to metal and somewhat injurious to concrete. It also has a harmful affect on plants and vegetation in its concentrated form, and causes steel to corrode. Consequently, it is used in galvanized, enameled, or other protected pans, screens, or trays.

Silica gel and lithium chloride have not attained as wide a usage in basements as has calcium chloride, presumably because their power of absorption is not as great. Silica gel, however, may be re-used if the gel is re-heated. A few mechanical dehumidifiers operate on a continuous cycle using silica gel. The heated moisture is vented to the outside.

Mechanical refrigeration dehumidifiers operate on the principle of condensing the moisture on a cooled coil called an evaporator. The temperature of the evaporator is maintained just above freezing. The basement is not cooled by this process, however, since the heat lost by the air is restored by blowing the same air through the condenser. This is an essential part in the refrigeration cycle. The condensed moisture, as water, runs down the coil into a container or drain. Electric power in a drain is needed to operate this method, but in place of a connected drain, a container may be used. The latter must be emptied frequently.

CHAPTER 9

BUILDING A DRY BASEMENT

It is about one-tenth as costly to build a dry basement as it is to correct water conditions after the house has been constructed. Proper planning and good workmanship, however, are essential. Effective use of waterproofing methods is not difficult to master. The amateur homebuilder will find it a simple matter to incorporate them with established building techniques.

Fig. 1. When planning to build a home, it is best to pick the highest spot on the property for the building site.

PLANNING

A dry basement is no accident. It was planned that way. The various factors which must be taken into account before building are extremely important, however. Bear in mind that drainage is the most important single factor affecting leakage and dampness in the cellar. Where natural drainage does not exist artificial drainage must be provided. In addition, special waterproofing measures and construction techniques may have to be employed. This will, of course, depend on the amount of exposure to water conditions, especially hydrostatic pressure.

Selecting the Site

Drainage conditions should be considered, if possible, before picking the spot where the house is to be built. If the lot is very small this may not be possible. But remember

that a dry basement can be built no matter where the house is situated.

If the spot is low and the surrounding terrain rolls toward the house, water can be expected to flow in the direction of the foundation walls whenever it rains or whenever ice and snow melt. A building on a hillside may also be exposed to water running down against one side of its foundation, or it may be in the path of water draining down from property above it.

It is always best to pick the highest spot on the land for the site of the building. If the land runs toward the road or is graded toward the road, it may be advisable to build the house farther back. This would provide more fall toward the road. If distance to the drainage outlet is

172

a more important consideration, the house should be set close to the road.

The selection of the site should include consideration of drainage outlets, natural and otherwise. Even if the ground provides poor drainage, water can be diverted from the foundation if a natural body of water or a storm sewer is close enough to provide an outlet.

Information from Neighbors

An easy way to obtain information about water conditions in a particular location is to question neighbors about their experience. Where neighbors will permit an inspection of their own cellars, these should be examined to see if floors are cracked. In addition, it will then be possible to find out what steps, if any, they have taken to offset hydrostatic pressure. Information may be obtained on general climatic conditions, soil composition, position of water line, location and characteristics of drainage outlets. It will also be important to know the whereabouts of drainage systems used by neighbors, since these might flow in the direction of your property.

If there are no neighbors or information cannot be obtained in this way, contact the State agricultural college. This institution usually has maps and data on soils and other conditions. The local town engineer may also have such data. If you have already obtained the land, the most accurate information on soil and water conditions will be obtained by examining the ground

Fig. 2. Dig an excavation to find out the soil condition of your property.

itself after the excavation has been made.

Soil Conditions

The composition of the earth may vary. The soil beneath a neighbor's foundation may often be quite different from yours. Individual borings are frequently inaccurate for the same reason. One hole may indicate a certain type of soil, while a second, only a few feet away, will indicate a completely different composition.

The best thing is to dig the excavation and examine the soil inside. It should be open and porous so that air and water are admitted readily and disposed of freely. Examples of such soils are sands, gravels and porous rock. A clay soil will tend to hold the water so that it builds up pressure. Even though the excavation may be perfectly dry when

Fig. 3. Hydrostatic pressure is indicated when water will not run off properly from an excavation.

ment will have to be thick enough to withstand the pressure of the water gathered in the 2 feet of clay soil before receiving the benefit of the natural drainage above. When clay is confined to the bottom of the excavation, it may be advisable to start building the basement a little higher up.

Examining the nature of the soil surrounding the foundation is important, because the basement surfaces are submerged in the earth. If the soil in contact with the walls and floor remains wet for any appreciable period, the moisture will find its way through openings.

Determining Hydrostatic Pressure

If the excavation is in a clay soil and also in a low spot where drainage cannot be provided, hydrostatic pressure will result. When the soil cannot be properly identified, take a hose and fill up the excavation with water. If the water does not run off properly, hydrostatic pressure is present. A combination of sub-surface drainage and waterproof construction will have to be used. If no drainage is possible, the construction must be made of sufficient strength to withstand the pressure.

Take for example, a basement which is to be 20 feet wide and 50 feet long, or 1,000 square feet in area. Examination of the excavation reveals that the bottom 3 feet contain a soil that will not have any natural drainage. Now the basement floor is literally displacing 3,000 cubic feet of water. Thus there is an upward pressure of 187,200

originally made, if it is in a clay formation water will collect when it rains. It is then necessary to drain the water from the foundation.

Almost all other types of soil can be broken up a bit to give some natural drainage. This is especially true where strata of rock are found. The water is usually drained out thr_ _ _ strata. Sometimes, however, water co _ _ es through the rock and enters the excavation. This happens when there are underground springs or streams. Gravel, however, always indicates natural drainage.

Frequently, an excavation will consist of a combination of soils. This has a bearing on the construction. For example, if the bottom of the excavation is clay, and about 2 feet higher a layer of gravel or sand is discovered, the floor of the base-

pounds. The basement and the superstructure must weigh at least 187,200 pounds, otherwise the house will have a tendency to float.

Concrete weighs approximately 130 pounds per cubic foot. Figuring the weight of the concrete in foundation walls 12 inches thick and in a basement floor roughly 4 to 6 inches thick, the total weight of the walls and floor can be determined. That figure subtracted from the 187,200 pounds provides the number of pounds the superstructure must weigh. If this instance were a ranch-type house of one story, with tile walls or a frame construction, there would probably not be enough weight to displace the water. The tendency would be for the building to shift around and cause damage to the walls.

Wherever proper drainage is not provided such a possibility exists. Footing drains, such as those described in Chapter 8 must be installed to relieve the pressure.

The important thing is to estimate the amount of water that must be displaced before starting construction. If sufficient drainage cannot be provided to reduce the pressure, the weight of the foundation and superstructure will have to be great enough to displace the water. Frequently heavier building materials must be substituted or the level of the basement must be raised.

Water Line

The water table or water line is the level at which the water ceases to run off. This can be correctly

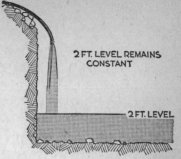

Fig. 4. The water line is that point at which the water ceases to run off no matter how much is added.

determined only after the excavation has been made. The water line cannot be determined at the surface of the ground.

If the excavation is filled with water and it never gets higher than 2 feet, regardless of how much water is added, that 2-foot level is the water line. Natural drainage is in effect at the 2-foot level.

Design

The design of the basement will have an important bearing on its dryness. The more openings through the walls, for example, the greater the possibility of penetration. Openings for gas, electricity and water pipes should be kept to a minimum and should pass through the walls well above the water line. This will reduce possible damage from water penetration. The design of footings and supporting columns may also have a bearing on watertightness. The more columns that penetrate through the floor, the greater the possibility of water seeping through joints. This trouble can be avoided if, instead of resting on footings below the floor the columns rest on the floor itself.

TYPES OF CONSTRUCTION

Stone, brick, concrete, solid or hollow concrete blocks, and very strong, dense, vitrified hollow clay tile are most commonly used in the construction of basements. Cost and availability of materials are of prime importance, but the purpose for which the basement is to be used is also a factor to be considered. A basement designed only for a heating plant, and possibly a laundry, will not require any particular architectural effect. A basement to be used in addition for a children's play room and a game room for adults must be built with some consideration given the decor or finish. Concrete walls, stone walls, or concrete block walls can all be finished with a cement plaster to give a surface on which a decorative paint or some other attractive cover may be applied, or the plaster itself may be treated with a stucco finish. A foundation made of stone, however, will often result in a very rough, uneven wall, and two or more coats of cement mortar must be applied until all of the recesses have been completely filled and a final straight surface obtained.

Concrete block or poured concrete are generally considered the cheapest and most effective for constructing foundation walls. There is a considerable difference of opinion among architects and builders as to which is more economical. Concrete block is usually less expensive, while concrete is more serviceable and dependable.

All concrete block walls have a tendency to crack from shrinkage, even though there may be neither hydrostatic nor earth pressure. The principal thing to bear in mind about shrinkage of concrete blocks is that shrinkage cracks frequently occur below the water line. This is especially apt to cause a water condition in the cellar. The crack must then be cut out and repaired.

Supporting the Walls

In constructing basements, the walls may be either supported on concrete footings or placed right on top of the foundation floor. The usual method is to pour concrete footings and build the basement walls on top of them. The footing extends beyond the wall on both sides and distributes the load over a greater area of the earth below.

When footings are not used, the basement floor is poured and the walls are built on top of the floor. The floor itself acts as a footing, and distributes the load. Also, the building is a self-contained unit. When there is movement, the basement floor and walls move as one piece, and a little settlement won't be noticed. When a house that has been built on footings settles, the tendency is to tear the masonry apart. A house built with the floor as a footing can shift the same amount without any evidence of cracking.

When a building settles, the cracks formed provide openings for leakage. Settlement occurs more often when a house is built on footings because water gets in the ground around the footings and washes soil away.

When a house is built on the floor pan, it is possible to build on a soil that will carry less of a load. If footings are installed in similar ground, they have to be either laid deeper or spread out wider. This entails digging a deeper or broader excavation, increasing the expense and adding to the water hazard.

Type of Floor

Where a cellar floor is below the ground water level and sufficient drainage is not possible, a concrete construction is generally recommended. The floor should be given a slight slope in one or two general directions. This will aid the removal of water if it should enter. Even if the basement is not to be used, some covering should be placed over the soil. This can be merely a layer of gravel or a topping of concrete. Where concrete is used, it is best first to cover the ground with a layer of gravel. The thickness of the concrete floor depends on the existence of hydrostatic pressure and availability of some form of drainage. If the hydrostatic pressure is great and drainage is not possible, a concrete floor reinforced with steel may be needed.

Wall Thicknesses

The local building codes state the minimum requirements for wall thicknesses. In general, however, for one- and two-story dwellings, cellar walls should not be thinner than 16 inches for rubblestone, 12 inches for brick, solid or hollow blocks, or clay tile, and 8 inches for solid concrete.

WATERPROOFING METHODS

In building a dry basement the problem is two-fold. Either the water must be kept away from the foundation floor and walls or it must be prevented from penetrating these surfaces when it comes in contact with them. In actual practice, a dry basement is usually achieved by a combination of methods.

Drainage

Where natural drainage does not exist, a sub-surface drainage system can usually be installed. When build-

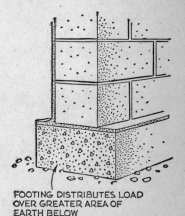

FOOTING DISTRIBUTES LOAD OVER GREATER AREA OF EARTH BELOW

Fig. 5. The drawing shows a wall built on a footing. Another type of wall is built without a footing, resting instead on the basement floor.

ing a basement this is always laid outside of the footings, as described in Chapter 8. Regrading the ground surface and providing sump pumps and dry wells are additional ways and means of diverting the water from the foundation. These are also explained in Chapter 8. It is very important that the home builder fully explore all possibilities for providing drainage before proceeding with construction. The availability of drainage will have an important bearing on the construction and need for additional waterproofing measures. If hydrostatic pressure is great, the amount of water taken off by the drainage system must be determined at once so that the building can be made strong enough to withstand the remaining pressure.

Fig. 6. Tools used in waterproofing include this homemade cord mop and old metal drum.

Membrane System

This is one of the oldest and most widely used means of waterproofing a foundation during construction. It involves wrapping up the walls and floor in a waterproof paper, or membrane. It can be used with any type of construction. Applying the membrane is not cheap and it requires hard work. It is not difficult to master, however, if instructions are followed closely. Sketches, specifications, and explicit directions should be obtained from a reliable manufacturer whose materials are to be used.

There are two distinct methods in use. The first consists of a floor installation covered with 3 to 6 layers of paper or felt, each sandwiched between moppings of hot tar or asphalt. A protective 4-inch brick or concrete wall is built high enough to form a backing for the wall membrane. The second method is to build the foundation walls on top of the floor membrane, applying the wall membrane on the outside surface of the foundation walls. The membrane is then protected with a 4-inch protective wall. This second method is the one generally used.

Before attempting the actual work, however, it is best to experiment with the materials. Select a small upright surface and practice the technique. If the membrane is not applied carefully the whole purpose of the work may go for nought. The principal materials are a bituminous saturated cotton or felt, which comprises the layers of membrane, and hot asphalt or coal-tar pitch, which bonds the felt to the surface.

A homemade cord mop should be used to apply the bituminous compound, and a kettle is required to heat it. The latter may be an old 50-gallon metal drum. Cut the head out and puncture holes in the side near the bottom to form a draft for the fire. Set the kettle on bricks about 6 inches from the ground, and fire it with wood.

Examine the felt to make sure it is free of holes, rents, cracks, indentations, or ragged edges. Any imperfections may provide openings through which water may penetrate. The asphalt and coal-tar pitch comes in solid forms packed in wooden barrels or steel drums. It should be cut out just as it is received from the manufacturer and broken up into small lumps. An axe should be used for this purpose. Following this, place the compound in the kettle and heat it to about 300 degrees F. Be careful not to overheat, as this tends to make it brittle when cold and destroys its cementing properties. Once the compound is fully melted and of uniform consistency, it will be an even glossy black. It should be used when it is in this hot liquid condition to give best results. Mopping must be done rapidly, otherwise the compound cools and loses its strength. It is better to install the membrane during warm weather. In cold weather greater precautions must be taken to maintain the necessary heat.

Before making any application, make certain the surface to which the felt is to be applied is smooth, dry and clean. Fill all holes and de-pressions in concrete or masonry with a portland-cement mortar. Brickwork should have struck joints. Knock off or scrape out any projecting stones or bits of mortar. These might puncture the membrane. Very sharp edges should be slightly rounded. The effectiveness of the membrane method depends a great deal on the nature of the surface it is wrapped around.

Spread a 1-inch underbed of cement mortar before laying the floor membrane. If water conditions are severe, spread a thin underbed of concrete evenly over the whole area. This should form a base upon which the floor membrane may be laid. Lay the floor and wall membrane as a unit. Lap and coat each strip of felt with the hot compound. Lay the strips across the floor and up to the wall in a continuous operation. It should proceed without a break at the wall angle and up the inner face of the protecting wall, in the first method, or the outer face of the foundation wall, in the second meth-

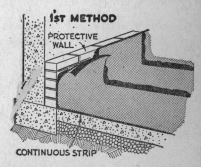

Fig. 7. When laying floor membrane, the strips should continue without break at the wall angle and up the inner face of the wall. This is the "first method."

od. After the membrane has been completely laid, a ¾ inch protecting layer of cement mortar should be spread over the whole floor area. Cover this with a 4 or 5 inch concrete floor. This must be recessed above the edge to lap and bond with the side wall. If the membrane is applied to the inside surfaces of the protecting walls, the main or foundation walls should be built right against the membrane. If the second method is used, the main or foundation wall is built on the floor. After the membrane is applied to the outside of this wall, build the outside protecting wall to prevent damage to the membrane. When the floor and walls cannot be waterproofed in one operation, precautions must be taken so that the strips of felt may be properly interlapped later on. Lay a 12-inch strip of the cement underbed along the footing course. Then bring the wall membrane down and over the footing course and underbed. Leave a 6 to 12 inch length of each strip of felt lying flat, and uncoated with compound, on the underbed. Turn up the uncoated laps after the floor membrane is laid. Then coat with the hot compound and interlock them with the floor sheets.

Determine the number of layers of felt to use by the seriousness of the hydrostatic pressure and the availability of drainage. When there is little or no head, and the main purpose is to dampproof, 2 layers of felt are sufficient. A minimum waterproofing application, however, will consist of at least 3 to 5 layers, depending on the height of the ground

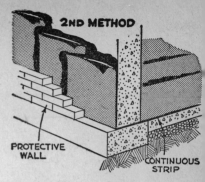

Fig. 8. In the "second method," the strips should continue to the outer face of the foundation wall.

water. Ends should overlap at least 6 inches. Mop evenly and fully, and be sure to spread the hot compound on each and every lap. As the mop applies the hot liquid, the felt should be unrolled and placed on the hot coating. Lay a strip at a time until every part of the surface to be treated has the required number of layers thoroughly cemented together.

To avoid a seepage seam between the felt and the masonry, the two must be united and bonded as effectively as possible. First give the masonry a penetrating priming of a suitable bitumen, applied cold. Approximately 1 gallon per 100 square feet should be used. Use a large, flat bristle brush, or a three-knot roof brush with a long handle, to expedite the work. If the priming coat is omitted, the hot compound is unlikely to stick strongly to the masonry because of quick chilling and slight penetration. The bond will be especially poor if the masonry is damp or cold. Mop the surface as soon as the priming coat sets and roll the

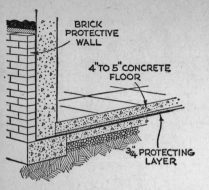

Fig. 9. The membrane should be covered first with a ¾" protecting layer of cement, followed by a 4" or 5" floor.

felt into it as previously described.

Be sure the felt lies perfectly smooth. Smooth out all wrinkles and buckles. Press the sheets down carefully and rub gently with the hand to remove air bubbles and to insure perfect bond between the felts. Use special care to make the felt fit corners and angles neatly and snugly. Such places should be reinforced. Take two strips of felt and cut them so they will extend at least 6 inches each way from the angle. Then apply one strip before and one strip after the main waterproofing membrane is placed. When several layers of felt have been cemented together, give the entire surface a heavy mop coat of the hot compound. Five gallons per 100 square feet gives a top coating approximately five sixty-fourths of an inch thick. Each coat between layers of felt takes about 3 gallons per 100 square feet. The mop coat over the primer on the masonry requires about 6 gallons per 100 square feet. This makes a total of 17 gal-

lons of compound per 100 square feet for 3-layer work, and 14 gallons for 2-layer work. In this way, a more or less pliable, yielding blanket or membrane, approximately one-third of an inch thick in 3-layer work, and one-fourth of an inch thick in 2-layer work, is built.

INTEGRAL METHOD

Where good drainage is available and there is little likelihood of hydrostatic pressure, water penetration can usually be prevented if good construction methods are followed and proper materials are used. A 1:2:4 concrete mixture, for example, will give a rich enough mix so that the cement will fill up most of the voids in the concrete and prevent penetration. This must be mixed thoroughly for at least 5 minutes before pouring. Unfortunately this is much easier to do in the laboratory than in actual practice.

To assist in making the basement as resistant to water conditions as possible, it is recommended that a waterproofing compound be used as a part of the construction material. This technique involves integrating a waterproof, chemical formula with the material. When a poured concrete is used, for example, the waterproofing is added at the same time the concrete is being prepared. With cinder blocks, or other pre-cast or baked units, the waterproofing compound is included in the mortar used to lay up the blocks, and in the protective plaster coating applied on either the outside or inside surface.

In the case of block, the plaster should be applied on both outside and inside surfaces.

Fig. 10. Mop evenly and fully, and be sure to spread the hot compound on each and every lap.

In Poured Concrete

From the standpoint of construction, the use of poured concrete for walls, as well as for the floor, is the most economical and effective method. An integral waterproofing added to the concrete, moreover, produces a wall through which water cannot penetrate.

Use a product with a national reputation. The mere fact that an integral waterproofing material is so called does not mean it will produce good results. There is no second chance. The basement will have been built before any test of its ability to withstand leakage is possible. There are many good products on the market. There are also many that are completely inffective.

When working with poured concrete, pay particular attention to the joints between the walls and floor. Sections or joints formed when a wall cannot be completed in one pouring must be handled with extra precaution. Wherever possible, cast a keyway in the wall at the point where the floor is to contact the wall. This can be made with 2 x 4" strips of lumber. Place a greased strip along the floor line in the concrete form. The concrete will run around the piece of wood. When the form is stripped, a recess will be left in the concrete. Then, as the floor is poured up against the wall, the concrete runs into the recess and the floor is keyed to the wall.

Whenever an integral waterproofer is used in a poured concrete wall, enough portland cement must be included in the mix to fill the voids of the concrete. Use at least 5.6 bags of portland cement for every cubic yard of concrete. This applies to a mixture of 1 part portland cement, 2 parts sand, and 4 parts stone.

Waterproofing compounds come in either liquid, paste, or powder form. If a waterproofing paste liquid is selected, mix it with the water which is to be used for wetting down the dry mix and forming the concrete. This can be proportioned according to the manufacturer's directions in a 55 gallon barrel or drum. If 1 part of liquid waterproofing is recommended with each 10 parts of water, simply add 5 gallons of the waterproofing material to the barrel and fill it up to the top with water. When the waterproofing compound is a powder, mix it thoroughly into the cement before adding the cement to the sand and stone. The mere addition of a water-proofing compound to the concrete will not have a magical effect, however. The construction's resistance to water penetration will still depend on the quality of the labor. Waterproofing is not a substitute for good workmanship.

Concrete should be poured when the temperature is favorable. Also, if there is water in the excavation, additional precautions must be taken. The floor of the pit must be kept relatively dry at the time the concrete is poured.

When groundwater drains into the excavation it must be removed while the work is being done. It should not only be pumped out during the time the concrete is being poured, but also for 24 hours thereafter. This will give the concrete a chance to set before the water can wash the cement out of the mixture. Always place the intake end of the pump at the source of the water so that the water does not have to travel across the excavation to get to the pump. If it does, it may carry some of the cement with it. Care should be taken to keep the flow of water under the concrete going to the intake of the pump. This may make it necessary to install drains to the pump.

Waterproofed Cement Plaster

When walls are built of blocks or brick or of any other building material that is pre-cast or baked, they should be laid up and covered with an integrally waterproofed cement mortar and plaster. Apply two coats of the plaster, each about ½ inch

thick. If the coats are made too thick, the plaster may slide down the side of the wall because of its own weight. The mixture should be comprised of one volume of portland cement and 2½ volumes of clean sand (1:2½ mix), plus enough water to make a plastic mix. Moisten the wall surface before applying the first coat. After this has partially set, scratch or roughen it before it hard-

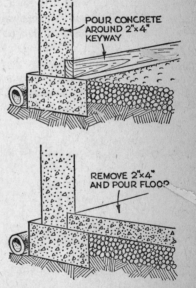

Fig. 11. When working with poured concrete, pay particular attention to the joints between wall and floor. Wherever possible, cast a keyway in the wall where the floor is to contact it.

ens, to provide a good bond for the second coat. Then let it harden for 24 hours, and apply the second coat. Keep the plaster moist for several days by frequent sprinkling with a hose. Before laying blocks on the footing, spread a 1-inch topping of cement plaster on the footing. This makes it possible to tie up the outside plaster with the waterproof inside floor. When it is time to apply the plaster start on the outside of the wall about 6 inches above the ground line. Continue down the wall and hook onto the topping made on the footing.

Thicken the cement plaster at the junction of the outside wall face and the footing. Then round it to form a cove. This will divert water away from the base of the wall. Do not allow any filling in of soil against foundation walls until the first floor is in place and the plaster surface on the earth side of the basement wall has hardened sufficiently to prevent damage.

Where a finish plaster of gypsum or lime is to be put directly on the inside surface of a basement masonry wall, the straightening coat of cement plaster should be waterproofed before the finish coat is applied.

In the case of hollow units, such as concrete blocks or cinder blocks, danger of leakage due to strong hydrostatic pressure may be reduced by filling the spaces with mortar. This has to be done only on the lower courses. It will not only strengthen the resistance of the wall to direct pressure but will prevent water from coming down through the hollow spaces above.

IRON WATERPROOFING

A third method of waterproofing when building a basement involves the use of iron filings. A mixture of filings and some chemical which will cause them to rust is applied. Mix it with portland cement and apply it as a cement plaster, in the manner just described, or make it into a semi-fluid mass and apply with a brush. The theory is that the iron filings in rusting occupy more space than in the form of natural iron and tend to fill up voids. This method has proved fairly successful.

WATERPROOFING JOINTS

While bituminous coatings are often suggested as a means of sealing up joints between walls and floors, this method is not recommended. The bituminous material and the concrete or cement mortar are different in substance. As a re-

Fig. 12. Provide a good bond for the second coat of plaster by scratching the surface of the first coat.

sult, they will expand and contract differently. This means that at certain temperatures there may be a tight bond between the two materials while at other temperatures there will be tiny openings through which water may penetrate. Use a cement mixture, therefore, on all cementitious materials to obtain the best results in sealing up joints.

DAMPPROOFING

Where sufficient drainage has been provided, there is little chance for hydrostatic pressure to build up around the foundation walls. It is then possible to use a dampproofing technique rather than a waterproofing method to prevent seepage and moisture penetration. Various dampproofing materials, discussed in Chapter 8, may be used. In addition, some of the heavier lead paints advertised for this purpose are satisfactory; they can be applied with a brush or spray. Where hydrostatic pressure is present, however, a waterproofing system and not a dampproofer *must* be used.

PREVENTING CONDENSATION

When a house is built in a region where condensation is known to occur frequently, preventive steps should be taken at the time of the original construction. Adequate ventilation should be provided and cold, exposed pipes covered. Arrangements should also be made to dehumidify the air and vent off

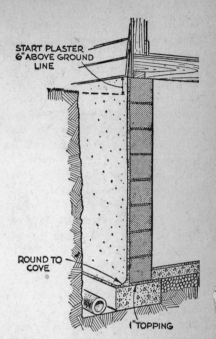

Fig. 13. Start the plaster on the outside of the wall about 6" above the ground line.

vapor-producing appliances. The interior side of masonry walls should be covered with a rough cement plaster surface to reduce the possibility of condensation or "sweating" walls, and, finally, insulation should be installed.

Insulation

Where condensation is known to affect the basement, an insulating material should be inserted in the walls and floor. It should be placed near the warm interior side of the masonry and protected with a vapor barrier. Use a rigid cellular insulation such as cellular glass or hard cellular rubber. Seal joints between the

Fig. 14. Where there is condensation in the cellar, cellular insulation should be used.

blocks of the insulation with a bituminous material. Place a strong wearing surface, such as reinforced concrete, over the floor insulation to distribute the load over it. Where condensation is a strong possibility, avoid using unprotected wood, metal, or other material that might be damaged by moisture inside the cellar. *See Chapter 5.*

BASEMENT FIREPLACES

If a fireplace is built in the basement, it is better to install the cellar floor first. Then build the fireplace on the floor. Many builders construct the fireplace first, and build the floor up to it. This is very bad practice if a water condition is present. The fireplace leaves a big square hole in the floor whereby water may easily enter and cause trouble.

WINDOW WELLS

When windows are installed below ground level, the cut-out area will form a pit or well alongside the foundation walls. The bottom of these wells must be drained, or water will accumulate and form a pressure against the wall or seep through openings in the frame. *See also Surface Drainage in Chapter 8.*

INTERIOR CONSTRUCTION

The foundation walls and floor should always be completed before any other kind of work is begun on the inside of the basement. This includes stairways and any partitions. Once the foundation walls and floor are built so they will prevent water from entering the basement, work may be begun on the inside.

Carpentry, electrical wiring, plumbing and other work must not be permitted to interfere with the waterproof construction. Holes cut clear through the walls will ruin the waterproofing. In the case of integral waterproofing, however, holes can be cut into the waterproofed concrete, provided they do not go through the entire thickness of the walls. Bolts or nails that are driven part way are merely imbedded in the waterproofed concrete and water will not come through. Caution should be taken in making such holes not to crack the foundation. A membrane system may be punctured by nails or screws. *For method of repair see Chapter 7.*

All openings made for electrical conduits, water pipes and other fixtures should be carefully sealed at the points where they penetrate the walls, both inside and outside. Moreover, these pipes should, if possible, be installed so that they pass through the wall at a point above the water line.

If the upper floors are supported on iron (lally) columns, it is always better to place the columns on the finished floor rather than to install them on separate footings below the floor. The reason for this is that wherever the metal passes through the concrete, the joints must be made watertight. This is often a difficult task. If the column is installed on top of the floor, no such joints exist, and the openings for sewage pipes may be the only penetration necessary below the water line. These can be sealed up with

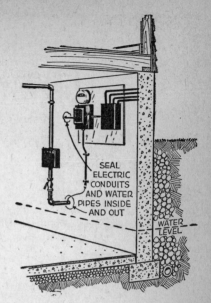

Fig. 15. All openings made for electrical conduits, water pipes, and other fixtures should be carefully sealed where they penetrate the walls.

oakum or any other material that is adaptable to caulking in irregular spaces.

CHAPTER 10

SUPERSTRUCTURE

HOW WATER GETS INSIDE

Wind-driven rain exerts a strong force on the walls above grade. When openings or cracks exist, the water naturally falls into them. It may seep through tiny holes, or pour in through open windows. The larger or more numerous the passageways, the greater the penetration. The only way to keep the water out is to make the walls waterproof.

Where water spills down on superstructure walls from the roof or adjoining surfaces, however, a drainage problem exists. In this instance water, or melting ice and snow, collects on the roof. Instead of the water being diverted away from the sides of the building, it pours against them. Weak spots are found or created by the pressure and leakage occurs, (Fig. 1). Such a condition must be remedied by improving or repairing the drainage system.

These two factors, plus capillary action and condensation, are the major causes of water conditions in the house proper. Capillary action brings on dampness in rooms above the ground by drawing up moisture from the wet soil around the foundation, or from standing water in the cellar. Condensation, on the other hand, does not involve any flow of water through surfaces. It contributes to dampness in the superstructure by depositing moisture on inside surfaces when certain atmospheric conditions are present.

Fig. 1. Wind-driven rain seeks out weak spots on superstructure walls and leakage occurs.

Rain Penetration

Rainfall is a constant threat to a building's dryness. Whenever it falls on the walls of the house it tests the resistance of the structure. The rain may fall directly through open spaces cut clear through the wall, from outside to inside. It may saturate the wall and be drawn into the interior by means of capillary action. Finally, it may penetrate the outside wall in one place, trickle down behind it, and seep through the inside wall at some other point. The latter possibility is the most frequent cause of dampness due to rain penetration.

The solid appearance of walls is deceiving. First, there is a finished wall on the inside which is continuous. Then on the outside, there is an architectural treatment, brick, stucco, shingle, or other finish. This also looks continuous. However, between the outside finish and inside wall there may be lots of crude open spaces. In fact, most walls are purposely designed with air space for insulating purposes. Water penetrating through faulty mortar joints, or other openings in the outside finish, consequently, can easily run around in the space between the outside finish and the inside plaster.

Faulty Drainage

When rain falls on the roof or adjoining surfaces it must be properly drained off, otherwise it will spill onto the masonry walls. This is also true when ice or snow collects on the roof and then melts. The flow of water may strike the superstructure walls unless it is diverted.

Improper drainage is a most common cause of dampness in the house proper. The water strikes the wall with considerable force because a stream has been formed from individual rain drops, melted ice, or snow. Dampproofing the wall will, at best, give only temporary relief. Proper maintenance and repair work on the drainage system is the only satisfactory solution. Remember that leakage due to poor drainage may often show up some distance from where the water enters the house. This makes it especially important to locate the source of the trouble before waterproofing.

Capillary Action

Dampness in rooms above the ground is sometimes caused by moisture rising up from the soil. This occurs when sufficient drainage of ground water around foundation walls is lacking and proper waterproofing measures have not been taken. Moisture is absorbed from the ground and drawn up into the walls. This may cause dampness at a height of 4 or 5 feet above ground level, while some materials have been known to draw the moisture as high as 20 feet.

Standing water in the basement can also be drawn up to the floors above by means of capillary action, (Fig. 2). The same phenomenon occurs when snow or ice is allowed to stand for any length of time on the roof. The moisture may be drawn through the exterior surface and down into the house proper, resulting in stains and other troubles.

Fig. 2. Capillary action will draw water standing in the basement into the upper floors.

Condensation

The most common type of condensation occurs on the inside face of windows when warm air indoors strikes the cold pane during low temperature weather. If enough water collects on the sill, it may leak down on the floor and cause a great deal of damage. Condensation may also take place on the inside face of a wall that is cold, around light fixtures on the ceiling, and on door and window hardware, such as hinges and doorknobs. Occasionally condensation also occurs on the outside surface of a masonry wall, causing blistering, peeling and dirty streaks on the paint.

When walls become damp during rainy weather only, moreover, it may be due to condensation, or from rain water passing through the wall. Droplets of moisture appearing on the inner face of the wall will make it difficult to determine the real source. It is advisable therefore to test for condensation as noted in Chapter 5.

Spilling and Leakage

A water condition can develop in the interior of the home if there are large amounts of water spilled on the floor. This occurs most often in the kitchen and bathroom and is readily observed. Sometimes water from the shower, however, leaks over the side of the bathtub, or sprays onto the bathroom wall. As a result, wet blotches may appear on the walls of floors below.

Leaky pipes or radiators' valves are another source of dampness in the house proper, (Fig. 3). Where pipes are exposed, the source of the difficulty is easy to discover. When they run through wall enclosures or are otherwise hidden, the solution is more complicated. In general, the same remedy used in repairing leaky pipes in the basement (see Chapter 4), will apply.

SIGNS OF LEAKAGE

When water conditions occur in the superstructure, actual stains or wet spots are visible. These are the principal clues for determining the source and cause of the trouble. Start with the stain or wet spot. Try to visualize what is behind the wall where the dampness appears. If water makes a stain near the ceiling, for example, it would be logical to suspect that leakage is coming from the floor above. The water might be running along the flood beam of the floor above, or a roof beam, if it is on the top floor, and coming in at the point where the beam rests on the wall. This does not, however, necessarily follow. The water might also be coming through a parapet wall, finding its way to a point where some piping is in contact with the wall. Then the beads of water could be carried along the pipe from the outside wall to the interior of the house proper. Thus, the signs of leakage must never be considered more than a starting point in determining where the water is coming from and how it is getting through to the superstructure.

As a rule, leakage which shows up under a window sill or around a window frame is caused by faulty caulking around the window frame. It may also be due to washed out mortar joints underneath. This takes place when continual rains over the years do not drain off the window sill as they should. Instead they run around the window sill and drip over the mortar below. Gradually the mortar begins to disappear. Thus it is a good idea to examine the mortar joints underneath the sill on the outside of the wall when stains appear inside near the window.

Sometimes, water leaking through window sills or frames may show up on furnishings. In one case where

metal frames were used, water came in at the top and appeared on the drapes hanging over the windows. At first it was believed that the windows, which were of the French type, did not fit properly. A hose was used to spray water on the surface. No leakage occurred either through the glass joints or the masonry around the window, but when water was played on a certain part of the window frame, it came through quite freely. This necessitated a lot of re-caulking around

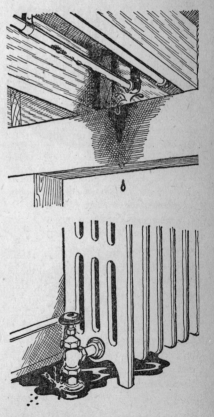

Fig. 3. Leaky pipes or radiators cause dampness in the house proper.

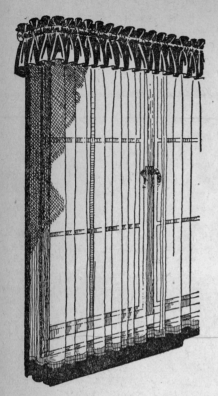

Fig. 4. Metal casings frequently must be re-caulked to make them watertight.

the window frame to make it water-tight, (Fig. 4). Because the water showed up at the top of the drapes, however, the owners insisted that the wall above the window frame might still be leaking. Yet when the window frame was protected with covers, and a 20-minute hose test was applied to the masonry work above the window frame, there was no sign of any water coming through.

Plumbing leaks are especially difficult to trace. The stain or wet mark may appear some distance from the

leaky joint or corrosion. The leak can be carried almost to the center of the room if it flows along a pipe that runs in that direction. Generally, the stain appears on the ceiling, but it might also show up on a bathroom floor where there is a corroded pipe. The floor must then be pulled up in order to locate the leak in the pipe. This type of leakage is an especially common occurrence, particularly in old houses.

When water finds its way to the inside of the superstructure, the spot where it appears is actually wet while the water continues to flow. In other words, while the rain, which might be the source supplying the water, comes down, the wetness will continue. When it stops raining, the spot will dry, but a stain will be left.

Spots due to pipe leakage might appear at different times, depending on the type of pipe. Leakage from a supply pipe, for example, might be continuous. On the other hand, leakage from a corroded waste pipe would only have a chance to cause trouble when water runs out through a wash bowl, tub, or toilet. The supply of water would be intermittent and leakage stains would only show up at certain times. Leakage from a steam pipe would only take place when the heating system was in use, and the water stain would only appear at that time. Sometimes wet spots caused by leakage dry out slowly. Thus the spot may remain damp for a short time, even after the supply of water has ceased.

It is important to use the signs of leakage only as a starting point in

way the condition is referred to as *spalling*. Spalled surfaces are always a sign that water has gotten in back of the surface of the wall. For this reason, mortar joints should be checked regularly. If it is discovered that they are opening up from shrinkage or other causes, or washing away because of a stream probably caused through a leak in the downspout, repair work should be undertaken at once.

EFFLORESCENCE

Sometimes a white, powdery, salty substance appears on the surface of masonry walls. This indicates that moisture is present within the wall itself, (Fig. 5). If this moisture is permitted to collect, it may lead eventually to the deterioration of the masonry. This condition is known as efflorescence.

Fig. 5. A white, powdery substance appearing on a masonry wall indicates that moisture is present within the wall itself.

trying to locate the source and cause of the wetness. Never proceed with repair work until the reason for the condition has been definitely determined.

Spalling

Water that gets inside mortar joints expands about one-eleventh of its volume when it freezes. This expansion creates a strong pressure, which will cause mortar joints to crack and break out. It may even cause the surface of the brick itself to break, because the water may get a chance to develop some leverage there. When mortar or brick is damaged in this

Causes of Efflorescence

On brick or tile masonry walls, efflorescence appears as a light, white powder, or crystallization. It may also take on the color of salts or impurities present in mortar, stucco and other masonry. It is most noticeable, of course, when it occurs on material such as red brick, and it is sometimes overlooked when it takes place on white-colored materials.

Efflorescence actually takes place when moisture comes in contact with certain soluble salts in masonry. When the water evaporates these salts are deposited on the surface of the masonry. Salts usually found in efflorescence are calcium sulfate (gypsum), magnesium sulfate (epsom salts), sodium chloride (table salt), sodium sulfate, and potassium sulfate. Efflorescence is produced when soluble salts are present in sufficient quantities in materials used to construct the wall and there is enough moisture present to bring these salts to the surface.

Soluble salts may be present in masonry units, or in mortar or plaster. Most newly produced structural clay products do not contain enough soluble salts to cause efflorescence. Second-hand brick, however, may often be a source of efflorescence when used in new construction. This is because it has an uncertain origin and usually previous contact with mortar or plaster which contain soluble salts. Portland cements contain soluble salts, as do some limes, sands, and even mixing water. Other masonry units, apart from brick, usually contain soluble salts too. When efflorescence appears only at the edges of the masonry unit, it is likely the mortar contains soluble salts, rather than the masonry unit. Should efflorescence cover the entire unit, both the masonry and the mortar are responsible. If it appears only in the center of the unit, soluble salts are in the unit and not in the mortar.

Moisture must be present in sufficient quantities to effect efflorescence. It is, therefore, important to trace the source of the water. Usually, the presence of moisture is caused by some fault in construction. However, when a uniform coating of efflorescence appears on a newly constructed building, such may not be the case. An excessive amount of water may have been used during building operations. While this moisture is in the process of gradual evaporation soluble salts present may be brought out to the wall surface. If the building is well designed and constructed, this condition is easily overcome. A final cleaning, or perhaps a few rains, will wash away the efflorescence and it may never reappear.

Should the efflorescence persist, however, moisture still penetrates the wall. Steps must be taken to determine the source of the water and eliminate it. Defective flashings (or the lack of flashings at vulnerable spots), clogged gutters and downspouts, faulty copings, or improperly filled mortar joints may, either singly or in combination, be responsible for the moisture and, indirectly, the efflorescence.

The location of the white powdery substance on the wall, however, does not always indicate the place where the water is coming from. The moisture could be penetrating at some other spot and leaving at the point where the efflorescence appears. The location of the efflorescence does nevertheless serve as a starting point in tracing the origin of the water. Efflorescence streaking down from the top of a wall, or patches some distance from the top would indicate defective copings, gutters, or roof flashings. If efflorescence is spotted under windows, investigate the sills and caulking around the window frame. A defective mortar joint, or a projecting course of masonry forming a water table, may also be the cause of a single patch of efflorescence if masonry openings, copings and gutters are not responsible. Sometimes efflorescence shows up on the foundation wall close to the ground. If especially porous units were used in the construction, this condition could be the result of ground water drawn up by capillary suction.

Correcting Construction Faults

The permanent solution to an efflorescence problem is to remove the excessive moisture. This should be done before any attempt is made to remove the powdery substance itself, otherwise it is likely to reappear again.

Repair faulty flashings, gutters and downspouts if they are the cause of the trouble. Where copings are at fault, take them up and relay them with thin, but well-filled mortar joints with rodded tooling. Place a non-corrosive metal or bituminous flashing directly under copings, cornices, chimney caps, sills and any projecting courses of masonry.

Rake out improperly filled mortar joints in exposed walls and repoint them with a plastic mortar of approximately the same mix as used in the original work. To eliminate as much of the original shrinkage as possible, the tuck-pointing mortar should be pre-hydrated by mixing with only a portion of the mixing water one or two hours before using. Then it may be remixed with sufficient added water to produce satisfactory workability. Avoid using cement, lime, sand or water which might tend to cause efflorescence. If there was no caulking

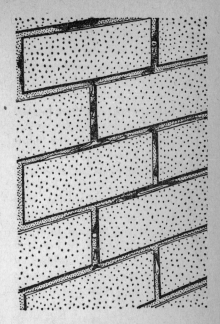

Fig. 6. Mortar joints are especially vulnerable to water penetration.

used around window frames and door frames in the original construction, this should be undertaken. Fill all cracks with a good elastic caulking compound applied with a pressure gun. Remove the original caulking if it has become dried out, cracked, peeled or separated. Replace it with a new compound. Raking and repointing the mortar joints in the sills may also be necessary.

Efflorescence found on the lower parts of walls above grade may be due to a lack of drainage, improper dampproofing or to capillarity. Footing drains may be installed and a dampproofer applied to the outside surface of the wall.

Removing Efflorescence

In new construction, as previously stated, efflorescence may disappear after a few rains. If it does not, the application of water with a stiff scrubbing brush will usually do the job. If this does not work, another method may be used.

First wet the wall. Then scrub it with water containing not more than one part of muriatic (hydrochloric) acid to nine parts of water. Pour the acid very slowly into the water when mixing the solution so that it will not splash up into the eyes and face. Immediately thereafter, rinse the wall thoroughly with plain water. It is very important to rinse the wall with water both before and after washing with the acid. Protect all frames, trim, sills and other installations adjacent to the masonry against contact with the acid solution. Wear rubber gloves and take precautions to protect eyes and exposed skin from contact with the acid solution.

The blotches may reappear again from time to time, and require additional washings. They will disappear completely, however, as soon as the supply of soluble salts in the materials has been exhausted. Colorless waterproofing compounds, applied to the surface of the wall to check absorption, will also tend to eliminate the formation of efflorescence.

On colored concrete, efflorescence, sometimes also called *blooming*, is particularly noticeable and objectionable. In addition to using the solution of muriatic acid, noted above, for removing efflorescence, it can be removed with a solution of equal parts of paraffin oil and benzine rubbed vigorously into the surface when the concrete is dry. This treatment also improves the wearing qualities of the surface by filling the pores and bringing out the color more uniformly. Thus it is frequently applied to concrete surfaces for these reasons alone.

POINTS OF PENETRATION

In general, water penetrates the walls above the ground wherever faulty workmanship or poor materials offer an opportunity. This fact emphasizes the importance of employing good materials and workmanship in new construction even if the cost is a little more. After the house has been built, or for older homes, the points of penetration can be kept to a minimum through proper and regular attention to maintenance and repair work.

Walls

Shrinkage or settlement may cause cracks in the walls. These will be quite visible. They offer an excellent point of entry for wind-driven rain, water from the roof, and moisture due to capillary action. In concrete construction, faulty workmanhip will sometimes result in weak spots or honeycombed portions. These are especially vulnerable to capillary action.

The mortar joints where blocks and bricks are laid up, however, are the greatest source of trouble, (Fig. 6). Little depressions are often formed in the mortar, either by the action of the weather, or during construction when the mortar slides after it has been trowelled in place.

A frequent location for water penetration lies in openings in the parapet, (Fig. 7). This is the extension of the wall above the roof. The water runs in at the ceiling of the top floor, or even farther down. It may enter the parapet because of driving rain either striking the inside or the outside, or there may be cracks in the copings through which the water penetrates. In this case, it will run through the center of the parapet wall. As a matter of fact, some copings are in themselves very porous.

The point where the top of foundation walls end and the masonry begins, and the juncture of the walls with the roof, are likewise common points of penetration for water. Wherever there are breaks in the continuity of construction, the danger of water penetration is greatest.

Windows and Doors

The installation of windows and doors breaks the continuity of construction and provides joints at which water often penetrates. At lintels, under sills, and around storm windows are especially vulnerable points. In addition, defective glazing sometimes permits leakage around windows. Condensation, too, is most frequently observed on the inside surfaces of frost-covered windows.

All joints, where the window and door construction cause a break in the solid wall, must be carefully sealed. Where the construction of a door is itself broken by a window, this portion must be treated as though it was a regular window in the wall. All joints must be properly sealed.

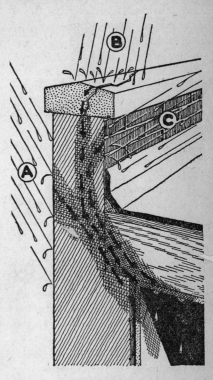

Fig. 7. Cracks in a roof parapet frequently allow rain seepage.

Floors and Ceilings

The vulnerable points for both floors and ceilings are the ends where beams rest on the walls, (Fig. 8), for in construction it is necessary to reduce the thickness of the wall on the outside of the beam to make sure the beams have enough bearing on the wall. As a result, a vulnerable point is created. Special care is then re-

Fig. 8. The points at which beams rest on walls offer slight resistance to rain unless protected.

quired during construction to make sure that the open spaces at the end, and around the beam, are properly filled in and protected. If not, water will penetrate through the reduced thickness of the wall at this point and run freely into the wall below. It may then be necessary to break out the wall at the end of the beam and fill it up solid.

Chimney and Fireplace

Water frequently penetrates into the interior of the house proper through the chimney. The latter may either rise inside the building and come out through the roof, or it may be built into the wall of the house and appear as a definite addition to the outside. Usually the chimney consists of a masonry material sur-

rounding a clay flue or pipe, which leads the fumes and hot gases from a fireplace or heater out of the house. The chimney must extend above the house itself, and certainly above the roof to prevent the smoke from discoloring the masonry and blowing back into the house windows. If a chimney extends very much higher than a roof it is because it was so designed to take care of a sufficient draft. As a rule, however, chimneys are higher than the required height for combustion purposes.

The masonry is exposed on all sides. Rain from any direction, therefore, can wet the chimney's walls. Furthermore, the openings at the top will permit rain to come down. For this reason, chimneys are equipped with a cap. This permits the fumes and gases to pass out, but it prevents the rain from coming down into the chimney itself.

The joints where the chimney meets the wall are the usual points of penetration. A chimney construction attached to a frame house is just about the same as a roof construction attached on top of a frame house. Water might stain the wall, or it might come in only when it gets down into the fireplace or heater where it will form a puddle.

Types of Construction

The points at which water is most inclined to penetrate varies a bit with the type of construction. Today, the great majority of new homes are of frame construction. The framework is covered with black building paper to act as a dampproofer. Architectural effect is applied as a veneer on the outside of the paper. The veneer may be stone, brick, shingles or stucco.

In the case of stone and brick veneer, the vulnerable spot lies in mortar joints, as mentioned before. With stucco, the entire surface may be porous if the stucco is lean in cement and rich in sand. Wooden sheathing or shingles, on the other hand, have weak points at the joints where one row overlays another. A driving rain may force water through by lifting or loosening a section. If there are any tears or openings in the dampproofing the water will then find its way through and stain the wall.

PREVENTING LEAKS

To remove the possibility of water entering the house proper, rain must either be diverted away from the walls, or the construction built so that it will withstand any water with which it come in contact. After houses have been completed, the problem is to keep roof water from draining against outside walls, and to maintain the surfaces of the superstructure so that there are no places where rain can drive or seep through. The following are methods of dealing with leaks after they occur. Ways and means of preventing water conditions during construction are described later within this chapter.

Drainage

Rain water striking the roof, or ice and snow melting on the roof, must be properly drained so that the water does not fall against the sides of the house. Where roofs are properly designed, arrangements are usually made to run rain water toward a gutter. This in turn is hooked up to a drain pipe which carries the water from the roof to the ground without touching the walls. If proper drainage has been omitted, it must be installed.

Where a drainage system gets clogged up, the water will run down the sides of superstructure walls. It is very important, consequently, to keep the drainage system open. Holes and cracks in gutters, leaders, and downspouts must be repaired promptly.

Flashings

Wherever the continuity of the roof construction is intercepted by a chimney, ventilator, or parapet wall, flashings should be used at the intersection. A flashing is a pliable but durable material made of metal. It is either bent or folded into place to prevent water from penetrating joints where the continuity of construction is broken. Flashings should be provided under copings, cornices, pervious or jointed sills, and projecting courses of masonry. Where parapet walls connect up with the roof, the flashing built into the roof surfacing must be extended upward to prevent overtopping by roof water, (Fig. 9). Then the flashing should be carried horizontally through the wall to within 1 inch of the outer surface. Provide undercut drips to courses which project beyond the vertical face of the walls. This will also help

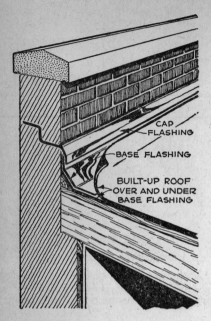

Fig. 9. Flashings must extend upward to prevent overtopping by roof water.

to divert water away from the walls. Where flashings are not used, joints in copings and cornices may be filled with mortar, or with plastic caulking compound.

Remember that water which penetrates defective or inadequate flashings on horizontal surfaces of masonry, may appear on the outside faces of walls at points far below and distant from the point of entry. Thus it is important to check the flashings, as well as the drainage system, before assuming that a water stain on a wall is the result of leakage at the spot where it appears. (Details on methods of installing and repairing flashings on the roof are given in the next chapter.)

Repointing and Filling

Cracks are usually due to poor workmanship, faulty materials, and building settlement. The latter causes a large, prominent crack, which extends across the surface of the wall and through the plaster. It may start at the corner of a door or window and run diagonally to the edge of the wall, or it may extend along the corner between two walls, or a wall and ceiling. It is due to the movement of the structural members of a building, and not to any fault in the plaster. Movements of this nature are a frequent occurrence, although a building and footings can be constructed so that the load is carried without any settlement. When settlement cracks do form, however, first let the building "find itself," and then point up the openings. Unless the structure is poorly framed, the chances are the cracks will not re-open, and the plaster will be better than new.

Cutting out and repointing mortar joints is actually the most effective method of stopping leakage. If the joints are properly maintained leakage may never occur. Unfortunately, proper attention to joints is often overlooked until a leak appears. Repairs are performed as follows:

Joints should first be cut to a depth of at least ½ inch, or to a depth about equal to their height. Secondly, they should be repointed, or filled with mortar. If the defective joints are not easily identified by a visual inspection, all the joints in the area should be cut out. Completely wet the whole surface of the masonry, as well as the joints, with enough water to prevent excessive absorption from the new mortar. Use a hammer and a cold chisel to perform the cutting, (Fig. 10). Where you have cracks in cement plaster or solid concrete walls, cut and scrape the edges of the cracks inward so that when the crack is filled with mortar, the mortar will be thicker inside the wall that at will be thicker inside the wall than at the surface.

When large areas are involved power tools may be more economical to use than hand tools. Care should be exercised to avoid damaging the mortar units. After the cutting is completed, remove all dust and loose material with a brush or a water jet. Mortar used for repointing, or tuckpointing, as it is also called, must not be denser than the mortar used originally in the joints. A rich mortar, thicker than the original, might cause excessive shrinkage and volume after it hardened. For the same reason, it is recommended that the mortar be pre-hydrated before it is used.

If the density and proportioning of the old mortar is not known, use a mortar mixed in the proportions (by volume) of 1 part portland cement (with not more than 10% hydrated lime), and 3 parts sand. Pack the mortar tightly into the joints in thin layers, and then tool it to a smooth, compact surface with a round jointer. If no jointer is available, use a quarter inch round rod with one end bent sufficiently so that it can be rubbed into the mortar joint without pulling the mortar out.

Repairs made to the sunny side

Fig. 10. Cutting out and repointing mortar joint is the most effective way to stop leakage. Use a hammer and cold chisel to perform the cutting.

of the house should be protected from the sun. Use a tarpaulin covering, or any other material which will shade the mortar until it sets. Canvas, for example, or even a wooden board, will do. Keep the surface damp. Sprinkle the wall with a hose once a day, for a few days. The slower the cement mortar dries, the better the results.

Cement-grout

When mortar cracks and openings are small, use a cement-sand-grout. Brush two coats of the application vigorously into the mortar joints. This is easier than repointing with mortar and is also an effective means of waterproofing the wall. If the cracks are large, however, cement mortar must be used.

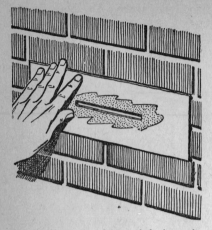

Fig. 11. Use a template to help keep the surface of masonry units free of grout.

A recommended mixture of grout consists of equal parts (by volume) of portland cement and dry sand passing a No. 30 sieve, with ¼ part of cement replaced by limestone flour, powdered fllint, or fine hydrated lime, with enough water to to give the consistency of thick cream. Wet the joints thoroughly with a stiff fiber brush before applying the grout. Use a template to help keep the surface of the masonry units free of the grout, (Fig. 11).

A template may be made by cutting a slit through a piece of thin waterproofing paper or oil board, such as is used for stencils in a shipping department. The slit should be as wide as the mortar joint. Then place the template, or guide, over the section of mortar joint that is to be filled in with the grout. Rub the grout over the surface of the paper, in through the slit, and onto the existing mortar joint. Use a shield to protect the brickwork from discoloration by the grout.

Whether a template is use or not, excess grout which gets on the brickwork must be removed. It should be wiped off the brick while the grout is still wet. Use a wet rag. Rinse it into a bucket of water repeatedly during the wiping process. This will keep the rag as free from cement as possible, and the brick will be fairly clean when the process is finished. Take care not to disturb grout deposited between the brick and mortar.

Do not use this method of repairing joints on rough-textured brick. If grout gets into a very rough texture, it is practically impossible to remove it quickly enough, even with a stiff brush. The cement will harden and discolor the rough-textured brick. A template can be used, if great care is taken in handling, but this is very difficult inasmuch as the rough texture of the brick prevents the paper from passing tight against the brick. Consequently, there is bound to be some leakage in between. The better procedure is to chip or scrape the mortar joint so that it recesses a bit, and then point it up with a mortar.

Where it is evident that water passes through the masonry units the surface may also be treated with a portland cement paint or a transparent waterproof coating. If the architectural effect must be retained, the colorless waterproofer should be used. Bear in mind, though, that these coatings will slightly change the actual color of the wall. In some instances they will slightly darken

o give better service with the use of primers. Priming is often done, but primers that thoroughly seal the pores are apt to interfere with the bond. Most types of primers produce discolorations on masonry if they are allowed to flow over the exposed parts, thus care should be taken when you apply a primer. Moreover, good mixtures which are non-staining usually do not require primers.

Since caulking compounds usually undergo changes in consistency, or dry out in the containers, they should not be kept in storage for long periods before use. It is better to purchase the caulking compound just prior to use. When caulking compound is left over, it should be covered with water and the can kept closed.

Caulking compounds often behave very differently in contact with building materials of widely different porosity characteristics. A type which might not stain limestone, for example, might act differently if used on some other type of masonry and cause stains. To be on the safe side, buy a caulking compound which is known to give satisfactory results on the particular material to be caulked. A simple staining test may also be made before applying the caulking compound. A small pat should be put on a block of the masonry material to which the caulking compound is to be applied, or a small section of a joint in an inconspicuous place can be filled. This should be permitted to stand for

about two weeks to note whether oil has spread into the masonry. If it has, another compound must be used. Testing is especially important when a caulking compound is to be used on marble, granite, or other materials which have a fine pore structure. Make certain that the surfaces on which the test is made are clean and dry. If the compound stains the masonry material for a distance greater than 1/16 of an inch from the line of contact, it should not be used.

The need for caulking around a window frame, doorway, or pipe cannot generally be determined by examining the surface of the joint. Discoloration of the interior of the walls, however, often indicates leakage around such places. This discoloration is formed when water picks up dust and other particles on its way to the interior surface of the wall. Later, when the water evaporates, this foreign matter is left behind as a stain or discoloration on the wall.

If examination on the outside indicates that the caulking compound has separated from the masonry even a little, however, it is usually better to re-caulk immediately, for that shrinkage, however tiny, means that the caulking compound has hardened and lost some if its elasticity to move with the masonry and the metal, or wood, that it is in contact with. In warm climates, or where the summers are very hot, caulking compounds dry out more quickly. Much depends, of course, on the quality of the product, and a high grade caulking compound should remain elastic for 10 or 12 years. A poor grade may last only a year, and then it may be necessary to do the job over again.

Before caulking around wood and metal frames, or between other materials of different kinds, cut openings between frames and masonry to a depth of at least ½ to ¾ inch deep. Deeper openings must first be packed within ½ inch of the surface with oakum or jute coated well with plastic roofing cement, or cement mortar, prior to use of the caulking compound. Stuff this material into the opening and hammer it in with a blunt-ended chisel or other piece of steel. In working with wood window or door frames and masonry, remove staff beads first. These are a sort of molding which closes the joint between wood and masonry. Use the oakum or jute to fill up all the openings around the frame. The caulking compound should be used to fill the space between the replaced bead and the masonry.

The porosity of the material in contact with the caulking, and the width of the joint, have an affect on the compound's consistency. Where metallic or other non-absorbent surfaces are involved, a stiffer consistency, or knife grade, should be used With stone or brick, a softer, gun grade consistency is used. Inspect work of this type after a few hours. If the caulking compound seems to be sagging, use a stiffer consistency.

Wider joints tend to sag if the material is too plastic.

Caulking can also be used to point up joints and seal cracks in plaster. Employ a compound of a stiff consistency suitable for knife application. Rake out joints or cracks to a depth of ½ to ¾ of an inch. Clean out thoroughly. Where the surface of the crack is porous, prime it or seal it with a shellac. Fill in the joint of the crack with the compound ⅛ of an inch beyond the surface. Then compress the compound thoroughly into the opening with a putty knife or blunt tool.

A knife-consistency caulking compound should be used to fill the joints between masonry units on the horizontal, or nearly horizontal surface of a wall coping, such as that formed on the top of a roof parapet. Fill the joint in this case to a depth of about ½ inch and finish it flush with the surface.

It is estimated that 2 or 3 average windows in masonry walls can be caulked with a quart of compound. In a frame construction, a quart will accommodate 5 or 6 average windows. When working with the caulking gun, incidentally, it is a good idea to press the hand grip while the nozzle is moving at a uniform rate along the crack to be filled. Use a piece of wood having a tapered or bevelled end, about ½ inch wide, to push the compound farther in and smooth it out. If the wood is kept wet, it slides more easily.

Portland Cement Paint

An entire outside masonry wall surface can be effectively damp-proofed with an application of portland cement paint. If the architectural effect must be preserved, however, this coating cannot be used because ordinary portland cement paint will have a gray or white color. Other color effects can be obtained, though, by thoroughly mixing or grinding not more than 5% of a mineral mortar color into the portland cement. In the case of a brick house, for example, if only one wall is to be painted, enough red portland cement mortar color can be added to the dry cement to give the painted wall the same color as the unpainted brick wall.

To make the paint, mix about one-half a shovel-full of sand to a bag of portland cement, with water and a liquid waterproofer. Where a waterproofer is not available, an ordinary mixture, without a waterproofer, can be used. For best results, however, it is best to add the compound. Follow the manufacturer's instructions for mixing and application.

Preparing The Surface

Before applying a portland cement paint, the wall must be thoroughly cleaned. This means that any paint, dirt, dust, oil and efflorescence must be completely removed. Use a wire brush to remove the grease or street dirt from the surface so that the paint can get into the pores. Do not use soaps or other organic cleaners because they may prevent proper adhesion if they are not completely washed away. Remove efflorescence as indicated in a previous portion of this chapter. Traces of form oil should be cleaned off with a steel brush or abrasive stones. If the wall is covered with other types of oil, remove it with gasoline or some other available thinner, otherwise the paint will not adhere.

Preparation of the surface, proper mixing with water, and applying the cement paint are the most important factors determining the effectiveness of the coating. The paint should be mixed to a rich creamy consistency, or one that can be carried on a brush, and applied with a brush in 2 or 3 coats. Where the application is being made on concrete units, or highly absorptive bricks, the first coat should have a slightly thinner consistency.

If the mortar joints are in very bad shape, they should be cut out and pointed up before painting. The portland cement paint itself can be used to fill small depressions and crevices in the mortar joints. The cement coating is worked in with the end of the brush. Instead of applying the paint with the full width of the brush, as is normally done, use the narrow side. Work it along in the direction of the mortar joint itself, horizontally and vertically, (Fig. 13). This will fill the cracks and holes with the cement paint.

The wall should be uniformly damp, but not soaked before the

Fig. 13. Apply portland cement paint in the direction of the mortar joint itself.

paint is applied. Use a garden hose with a fog nozzle, or a clean brush and a bucket of water for this purpose. The paint can either be sprayed or brushed on. Spraying is easier, but it must be done expertly to be effective. It is recommended, therefore, that the work be done with a brush with relatively short, stiff fiber bristles. Use a rotary motion in scrubbing so that the paint is forced into the open texture of the units and the mortar joints.

Never use less than two coatings, and, in many instances, three coatings are advisable. This is especially true when color is to be added. Apply the first coat without any color to give the strongest and most dense coating. The two succeeding applications will cover the gray of the natural cement paint and give the desired color.

Weather Restrictions

Do not put a portland cement paint on a frozen surface nor apply it when the temperature may go below freezing. If it is put on a frozen surface, the moisture in the wall, when released, will wash out all of the paint. Moreover, if the cement paint should freeze shortly after it is applied, the water will be removed from the mixture and the paint will not adhere.

Stir the paint continuously when applying it, otherwise the sand and cement will fall to the bottom of the container. Apply thin coatings as opposed to extremely heavy applications which will not stick. As soon as the first coat of paint has hardened, it should be cured by keeping the surface damp for at least 24 hours. This can be done by spraying at regular intervals. In the winter, however, when there is a possibility of freezing, do not apply the water until the weather permits. In warm weather the difficulty is that the water may evaporate too quickly to perform its function of hydration with the portland cement. In that case, the surface should be kept damp with a spray until the period of hydration is over.

Allow at least 24 hours between coatings. Then, just before applying the second coat, wet the surface down again. When the second coat has been applied, moisten the surface after the cement-paint has hardened sufficiently to prevent marring the surface. Keep it damp as long as practicable, but not less than 2 days. To avoid the danger of rapid evaporation of the water in hot and windy weather, keep the surface wetted down and try to do the painting in the shade rather than in the direct rays of the sun.

Before applying a portland cement paint to a stucco finish, first check on the condition of the stucco. Test it with a hammer to determine whether there are hollow sections where the stucco is not properly bonded to the underlying masonry, (Fig. 14). If this is not done, a section that is hollow may break off the building with all the brush coats on top of it. Where hollow places are discovered, the faulty stucco should be removed and fresh stucco applied before coating with cement paint.

Take extra care to work in the brush coat on rougher textures of surface. Wet them down more, too, because they will absorb more water from the paint. Extremely smooth or glazed surfaces will not accept portland cement paint very readily. A smooth brick that is hard burnt, such as fire brick, for example, will not absorb enough of the water to permit the cement to get into the surface pores, hydrate, and fasten themselves to the brick itself. An enamel brick, too, will have no adhesive value. If a cement brush coat is applied to these two types of brick, the only places where the paint will really be bound to the wall will be at the mortar joints.

While commercial preparations of portland cement paints are available,

Fig. 14. Tap with a hammer to test whether stucco is properly bonded to underlying masonry.

it is generally more economical and effective to prepare the mixture on the job. The commercial preparations require care in storage and are never as fresh as a homemade mixture. If one is purchased, however, be sure it is a portland cement paint, not merely a cement paint, which is not a waterproofer.

STUCCO

This is a very effective dampproofer made of portland cement and sand plaster. It may be applied like any other cement plaster —

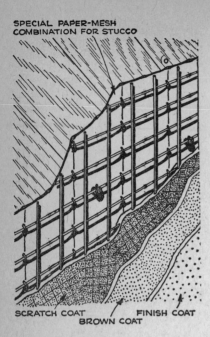

SPECIAL PAPER-MESH
COMBINATION FOR STUCCO

SCRATCH COAT / FINISH COAT
BROWN COAT

Fig. 15. Stucco paper has a wire mesh woven into it around which cement plaster wraps itself.

spread out with a trowel or wood float over the vertical surface to be protected. Stucco is not only a good method of preventing water from penetrating through the walls of the superstructure, but it is also an attractive covering. Today, the majority of low-price houses are built with a stucco finish. This is an economical way of obtaining a decorative and architectural effect. Stucco keeps out driving rains much more effectively than portland cement paints. When the cement plaster is dense, it will last for a very long time. Water will not be able to get into the outside wall and freeze as

happens with a porous surface. Thus spalling is less likely to occur.

On Frame Buildings

Stucco may be used on a wood-frame building or on masonry walls. When it is applied to a wood-frame building, a special dampproof stucco paper must first be put over the woodwork. This paper is available from all building supply dealers. It comes with a wire mesh woven into it so that when the cement plaster is applied, it wraps itself around the wire mesh, (Fig. 15). In this way it is held mechanically in place on the wires, where it sets and hardens.

Another method of applying cement stucco to frame walls is to first apply a black building paper to the wood and then nail on a metal lath over it. This lath is a perforated, or deformed metal. It is applied in sheets and should be attached with a wide head nail, or galvanized washer, so that it does not tear the building paper. When the cement plaster is put on the lath it finds its way into the openings and perforations. Then it sets up and hardens around the metal.

Sometimes, an ordinary wood lath is used instead of the metal type although it does not work as well. The stucco will be free from cracks on a metal lath, but when it is applied to a wood lath, or permitted to touch wood anywhere along its work, there is a possibility of cracking through the stucco. This results because wood absorbs the moisture and causes a certain amount of swelling. That pressure will push the stucco and crack it. Consequently, wherever any woodwork comes in contact with stucco because of the nature of the construction to which the stucco is to be applied, precautions should be taken. Cover that part of the woodwork with a black building paper. This will insure a little space between the wood and the stucco after the cement plaster stucco has set.

APPLY GROUT WITH A BRUSH

Stucco can also be applied directly to solid masonry walls. Clean and prepare the walls in the same manner previously recommended prior to the application of portland cement paints. All foreign matter, such as oil paints or white wash that may have been previously applied, must be completely removed from the surface. Then wet the surface down with water. Apply a grout to the wet wall. This can be made by stirring portland cement into a sufficient quantity of water to give the consistency of a heavy cream. It should be applied over the surface with a brush. While the grout is still wet, apply the cement plaster stucco with a trowel and float it solidly into place, (Fig. 16). The first coat should be scratched to receive the next coat.

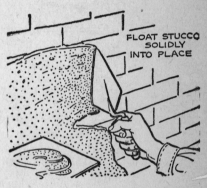

FLOAT STUCCO SOLIDLY INTO PLACE

Fig. 16. While the grout is still wet, apply cement plaster stucco and float it solidly into place.

Mixing Stucco

The cement plaster stucco is made by mixing one part portland cement and three parts of screened sand wetted down with enough water to give the proper consistency of a plaster which is applied to a vertical wall without sliding. A small amount of hydrated lime, not more than 3% by weight of the portland cement, may be added to give more workability to the mortar. While most stucco is applied without a waterproofer, it is recommended that one be added. It will add years of life to the stucco. In addition, it serves to prevent rain from soaking into any part of the surface and subsequently freezing in the winter time. The waterproofer should be in liquid form and must not be a water-repellent.

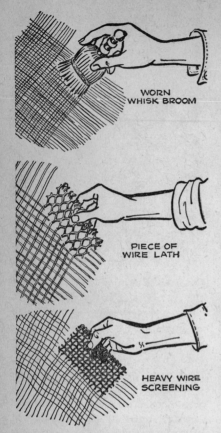

WORN
WHISK BROOM

PIECE OF
WIRE LATH

HEAVY WIRE
SCREENING

Fig. 17. You can scratch a stucco coating with a whisk broom or other implement.

Stucco should be applied in not less than two coats. The first coat should be thoroughly floated and scratched in two directions to leave a rough surface to which the second coat can key itself. The scratching, (Fig. 17), can be done with a worn down whisk broom, a piece of wire lath that has a lot of short ends to it, a heavy piece of wire screening, or anything that is stiff enough to scratch the surface with-

out wearing down too quickly, or bending out of shape so that it loses its utility too quickly.

Wait at least 24 hours before applying the second coat. It should be applied to a grout in the same manner as the first coat, and it may be finished with any desired texture.

It can, for example, be textured with a dash-coat and gravel mixed together to the consistency of a grout or paint. To do this, cover a stiff broom or brush, such as a whisk broom, with the semi-liquid mixture. Then throw it at the surface of the wall from a distance which is determined by the kind of finish wanted. The closer the brush is to the surface of the wall when the mixture of cement and gravel is thrown at the surface, the larger the dashes will be on the wall. The farther away the brush is, the smaller the dashes will be because they will have a better chance to separate from the brush.

Another method of texturing the surface is to press the palm of the hand at regular intervals in the soft plaster, (Fig. 18). The surface can also be rubbed with various materials, such as pieces of burlap or finer woven fabrics, or it can be worked into a fairly uniform design with a steel trowel. This is held at an angle and pushes the cement plaster away from the surface instead of holding it in, as would be the case if a smooth wall was desired.

A very effective finish can also be produced with a wood float. This is rubbed over the surface of the soft plaster. Then, instead of sliding it off the surface, it is pulled away at right angles to it. This causes suction in the spot directly under the float and gives a characteristic and distinctive finish.

Stucco is a very common finish for architectural effects and may be used over an entire wall. It may likewise be used in connection with some wooden trim, as in the old English type houses where different effects are desired over certain portions of the dormers, or even on the walls of the lower floors. The stucco is then brought up to the surface of the wood trim, and the wood is painted any desired color to contrast with the gray of the stucco.

If the stucco is on solid masonry and there are leaks, the first thing to look for is stucco that has not been properly bonded to the masonry. This can be located by sounding the surface with a hammer. When it is bonded tightly, the hammer produces a ringing sound; if it is not bonded, a hollow sound results.

TRANSPARENT DAMPPROOFERS

Where the surface of the masonry wall is giving trouble and it is desired to retain the texture or architectural appearance of the wall, whether it be brick, stone or stucco, the dampness can be stopped and the trouble overcome very often by the application of a commercial

Fig. 18. Another method of texturing a coating is to press the palm of the hand at regular intervals into the soft plaster.

transparent dampproofer. This coats the surface and soaks into the porous material without hiding what is underneath. These transparent dampproofers are all water repellents. They have no filling property. As a result it is necessary to fill or point up any cracks and holes in the stucco or mortar joints before applying a transparent dampproofer.

Transparent dampproofers are of various compositions. Some are paraffin oils, others are silicates, sometimes obtained as a by-product in the manufacture of glass, and others may be resins. All transparent dampproofers tend to darken the appearance of the surface a trifle. Consequently, use them with great caution on white walls, or very light walls where it is desired to keep the original color appearance. On darker colored walls, such as ordinary brick walls, however, the color of most transparent dampproofers will be

Fig. 19. A dampproofer can be applied to walls with a spray or brush.

difficult or impossible to detect at all, provided that the entire side of the building has been treated.

To apply, prepare the surface of the wall in the same manner as previously prescribed for cement paints. The dampproofer can be applied with a spray, (Fig. 19), or brush. A satisfactory spray coating can be completed in one application if the operator is able to tell when the surface has been treated with sufficient material. Brush application requires a minimum of 2 coats, and is recommended to the homeowner who has not had much experience working with a spray gun.

The main advantage of these applications is that you can stop seepage through a wall without changing the appearance of the outside surface. Transparent dampproofers are commercial products and should not be made on the job. They also require careful handling.

COPINGS AND PARAPET WALLS

In many homes, especially in buildings with relatively flat roofs, the wall is extended above the roof for several feet. This is a good safety practice. It serves as a fire stop and safeguards people, who walk on the roof to hang up wash or for various other purposes, from falling over the side.

The parapet is the only part of the wall which is exposed on both sides to the weather. This makes it necessary to prevent rain from entering either side and going down into the wall below the roof line through capillarity. The outside of the brickwork should be protected in the same manner as the outside of the walls below. The mortar joints should be solid. A protective coating of some sort may also be applied to keep the water out.

The outside of the parapet wall is part of the architectural effect and must be treated in the same manner as the outside of the wall below. The inside of the parapet wall, however, is also exposed to weather and sometimes, to a limited degree, to hydrostatic pressure if water accumulates on the roof. Since this side of the wall is not visible from the street, it can be treated with any type of coating found most suitable for the purpose.

Use a black tar or asphalt coating. Paint, (Fig. 20), or trowel it on to the inside surface of the parapet. This provides good protection. It also gives a surface on which the roofing can be brought up at the parapet wall to prevent leakage at the joints between the roof and the wall. The only vital spot then exposed to the weather is the top of the wall which should be protected with a coping.

The coping may be a tile of some sort, or it may be a series of precast concrete sections. These extend beyond the wall itself with an overlap of an inch or two on either side of the wall. Another form of coping consists of sections of blue stone laid end to end on top of the wall.

In every instance the coping should be placed on top of a bed of mortar made of 1 part portland cement and 3 parts sand. Joints between each section of coping should be filled with the same mortar.

When trouble from leakage through a parapet wall occurs, the water will find its way down into the floors below. This may be due to the fact that the only mortar used when the brick was originally laid up was a little buttered on the outside. Any leakage through the mortar joints connecting the successive sections of coping, therefore, would meet no resistance. Water could easily soak its way down through the brickwork. This is a frequent occurrence. Thus, never attempt to correct leakage through parapet walls, without first making certain that the coping does not have to be removed and reset in cement mortar.

PREVENTING DAMPNESS IN NEW CONSTRUCTION

When plans are laid out for a new house ascertain that proper provisions are made to dampproof the superstructure. Plans for caulking, flashings, and other protective measures to keep water out of the house should be made in advance. It is much simpler and less expensive to include dampproofing measures in new construction rather than to correct a water condition after the house has been completed.

Dampproofing

The particular kind of dampproofing to be applied depends on the design and materials of construction.

Fig. 20. To protect the inside of a parapet wall paint it with black tar or asphalt coating.

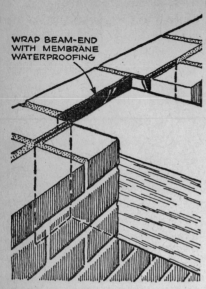

WRAP BEAM-END
WITH MEMBRANE
WATERPROOFING

Fig. 21. When a floor or roof beam sets into a brick wall, the best protection is to wrap a membrane waterproofing around the outside end of the beam, and imbed both ends of the membrane in with the brickwork.

In a frame house, a black building paper can be applied to the inside surface of the walls to keep moisture from coming through from the outside. The air space in between then acts as an insulator and barrier.

In a solid masonry wall made of brick, stone, tile, or block, the inside surface may be painted with an asphalt or tar paint, or bituminous coating. These coverings prevent moisture, which might penetrate the outside wall, from getting through to the inside finish plaster. The finish of the wall will either be made on strips of wood, covered with wall board and plaster, or on metal lath attached to wooden strips and plaster.

In the case of solid masonry walls, however, the finish plaster can sometimes be applied directly to the inside of the wall. This makes the room larger than when wood strips and lathing of some sort are installed prior to applying plaster. Where a plaster is applied directly to the inside of exterior masonry walls, a black asphalt paint can be used as a dampproofer. It should be mixed to a consistency which will remain tacky for a long time and not harden with a glaze. It must be applied to the wall before the plaster is spread on. These dampproofing materials are known in the trade as "plaster bond." They are used only for facing the inside of masonry walls to receive some gypsum or lime plaster.

Spandrel Waterproofing

When floor beams, or roof beams, are set into a wall the joints around the hole into which the ends are plugged are extremely vulnerable to water penetration unless they are properly waterproofed. The thickness of the section of wall where these beams are joined is reduced when the recess for the beam is made. Consequently, at that point the width of the wall is reduced by about one-half or more. If water gets through at this point it can cause serious trouble. The moisture will rot a wooden beam and rust a metal one, and in both cases the water is likely to run along the beam and leak inside the house proper.

Repairing a leak of this type is difficult and costly. The mortar joints must first be carefully examined. If they cannot be corrected, the brick along the cross-section of the beam in the wall must be removed. Then the hole should be completely filled with mortar.

It is better to do the job right in the beginning, however. Simply wrap a membrane waterproofing around the outside end of the beam, and imbed both ends of the membrane in with the brickwork, (Fig. 21). Water that might get in through the wall is thus diverted from the inside of the house. Felt or sheet metal can be used. The metal comes in pre-formed sheets, and the felt can be fitted on the job. Cut the latter with a sharp-edged knife. To make the felt adhere, use layers of felt and tar, or felt and asphalt, applied cold.

Remember that the weak point to be protected is the space left after the beam is set in the hole or recess in the wall. If the hole is a large one, masons will frequently throw in pieces of broken brick or other extraneous material to fill it up. The space should be filled up solid, however, with cement mortar.

PREVENTING CONDENSATION

In the house proper, condensation is most often caused by steam given off from water used in washing or cooking. The mere fact that living quarters are likely to have more persons in them also contributes to excessive humidity and condensation. In most instances condensation can be reduced by providing proper ventilation.

When building a home in an area where condensation is known to be a frequent cause of water damage, however, additional precautions are recommended. For complete details see *Chapter 5, Condensation.*

CHAPTER 11

THE ROOF

Fig. 1: The best materials and good workmanship are need in roof construction to check the damaging effects of the weather.

Roofs are built and designed to keep out water; proper drainage arrangements are usually made to lead roof water away from the foundation. Since roofs are exposed to strong winds, snow, freezing temperatures, and scorching sunshine, (Fig. 1), it is sometimes difficult to maintain this condition. Good materials and competent workmanship during construction naturally increase the durability and life of the roof, but even the best made roof will ultimately be affected by the natural elements. Proper maintenance is consequently necessary regardless of how well the roof is built.

A roof is composed of two parts, the covering and the deck or frame. Water penetrating the covering, will not only injure the house proper, but may well weaken the structure of the deck or frame. The roof covering should be inspected regularly, and if signs of deterioration are visible, repairs should be made promptly.

Working with Safety

Always wear tennis sneakers, or rubber or crepe-soled shoes for roof work. Never go up on the roof after a rainfall, as the surface will be slippery and dangerous.

If you must work on a roof where no special means of support exists, tie a rope around some solid object such as a chimney or soil stack. If this is not convenient, the rope can be run through an open window and fastened to some firm object indoors. For regular repair work, it is more convenient to have a special ladder available for this purpose. Any long, straight ladder will suffice if it has some means of being hung from the roof's ridge. This is usually accomplished with hooks, or pieces of wood nailed to the end of the ladder at about the same angle formed by the slope of the roof. A homemade device known as a "chicken ladder," or "chicken walk," can also be used. This is simple to build.

Take a stout plank or flat board at least ten inches wide and nail short wooden strips, slats, or cleats about one or two inches thick to the board at intervals approximately one foot apart. For support, one end of a rope can be fastened to the ladder while the other end is tied around the chimney or other safe anchor, or the rope may be thrown over the roof top and made fast on the other side. The best way, however, is to make a cradle or support for the ladder. To do this take two strong pieces of wood and nail one to each side of the ladder, near the upper end. Fasten the wood at an angle

Fig. 2. Repairing of rooftops is made easier by the use of a "chicken ladder."

with the legs. This will provide a hook or cradle which can be laid over the top of the slope to give the ladder something to hang or lean down from. The angle should be made as close to the slope of the roof as possible. It is also advisable to brace the pieces which form the cradle, or hook, by nailing short boards between them and the legs of the ladder.

Where to Look for Leaks

If you have an unfinished attic you can generally get a pretty good idea of where the water comes through the roof by observing the leakage around the rafters during a rainfall. It is also possible to detect openings in the roof by looking up through the interior on a bright day. When such holes or openings are discovered they should be marked. Do this by sticking nails, hairpins, strips of straw from a broom, or pieces of wire through the openings. It does not really matter what material is used as long as it is thin enough to be pushed through from the inside, and long enough to be visible once you get up on the roof.

If you have a finished attic, the location of the leaks must be esti-

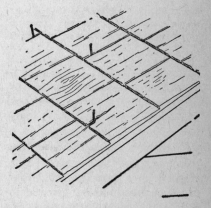

Fig. 3. Mark small holes in your roof by sticking strips of straw from a broom through the openings so they may be seen from the outside.

mated. Some clue is given by the location of the stain in the house. Then, when you actually go up on the roof, examine that portion of the covering which appears to be directly over the spot where the leakage occurred. The point where the water appeared inside the home, however, is often some distance from the hole in the roof through which it penetrated thus it may be necessary to search for the source of the leak over a considerable portion of the roof.

Sometimes it is advisable to remove some of the covering over the roofing material. When the roof is exposed in this manner, look for blisters. These are hollow spots that raise up in certain sections like little igloos. They are caused by seepage beneath the shingles. If the water in them is allowed to remain it will gradually penetrate into the house. Wherever these blisters occur, they should be severed with a knife and pressed down so that all the water between the layers is squeezed out. The section should be re-covered with roofing material and patched to prevent seepage.

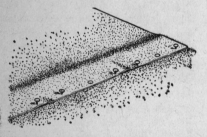

Fig. 4. Corrosion acting on exposed nails sometimes causes leaks.

Causes of Leakage

The demand for new housing following World War II made it necessary to build large numbers of homes as quickly as possible. Consequently, workmanship was often sacrificed for speed and many of the new homes have roofs that do not give proper service.

Even when a roof is well-made and quality materials are used, normal weathering will cause deterioration and prompt leaks. Poor materials will hasten leakage problems. When unseasoned lumber, for example, is used in roof-deck or frame construction, the wood often warps and tears the roof covering loose. Once this happens, the wind is able to pull it up completely.

If materials are used improperly, leakage is also encouraged. Asphalt prepared rolled roofings will not perform satisfactorily when used on slopes of less than two inches per foot. Likewise, wide-selvage roofing must not be used on roofs that have relatively flat pitches.

Exposed nails frequently cause leaks. Corrosive action causes them to rust and loosen sufficiently to permit rain to infiltrate through the tiny openings thus formed.

All joints where different materials meet on a roof, or even where similar materials form a juncture, offer major possibilities for water leakage. At such places, for example, where the chimney and roof come together, or where a vent pipe extends through the roof, joints are formed and water has an opportunity to seep through if proper precautions are not taken. Dormer windows, hatchways, and skylights are additional places where the continuity of roof construction is interrupted.

Joints are usually protected by flashings. If these are faulty or poorly installed, leakage is likely to occur.

These are the principal causes of water leakage through a roof. They must always be properly identified before any remedy is undertaken, otherwise time and money may be wasted.

REPAIRING LEAKS

In general, leaks which occur through the roof are repaired by patching the hole or opening, or by removing the defective flashing or shingle and replacing it with a new one. Repair work should be considered a regular part of the maintenance operation around the home, as tiny leaks will spread and an inexpensive patching job left untended will develop into a major repair job which will be very costly. The drainage outlets on the roof must also be kept in operation, otherwise dampness and leakage may occur in the floors below. Moreover, improper drainage might create hydrostatic pressure on the roof and this could force water through the covering.

Roofing Cements

To patch holes, cracks and joints, roofing cements are used. These are commercial products which come in plastic form and are applied with a knife or trowel. They are bituminous compounds made of oils, gums, asbestos fiber and various types of selected asphalts used to seal and patch flashings around chimneys, skylights, dormer windows, or wherever joints require waterproofing. Usually roofing cements do not re-quire a thinner. They have the same consistency as putty and are applied so that the covering is approximately ¼ inch thick. Roofing cement should overlap about one inch on all sides of holes or cracks. When the hole is larger than one inch in diameter, however, it should be reinforced with a piece of asphalt-saturated felt or burlap, first coated with cement on both sides.

FLASHING

Flashings are strips of metal used to waterproof joints between various structures that break the continuity of the roof construction. When flashings are improperly applied, or when the material of the flashing itself deteriorates, or if there is some movement of the structure to which the flashing is attached, leakage may occur through the joints. Consequently, whenever wet spots occur on the interior surface of the house, flashing near the spot where the water appears should be checked. Oftentimes the difficulty may be merely due to the flashing having come loose. On other occasions, however, the problem may be more serious and the flashing itself may have to be repaired or replaced.

Flashing is always exposed to the weather. As a result, it should be made of a non-corrosive metal such as aluminum. If it is not, it must be treated regularly or it will rust.

Flashing materials are easily bent or formed to fit any angle or curve. In addition to aluminum and galvanized iron, flashings are also made of slate, sheet copper, tin or terne-plate, soft lead sheets, and felt. The non-corrosive metals, such as aluminum, are finding increasing favor because they are attractive and do not require maintenance. Incidentally, aluminum will not stain the materials and paint work with which it comes in contact.

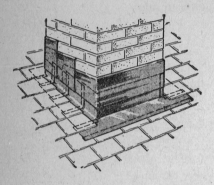

Fig. 5. Better joints are formed when the edge of the flashing is forced into a joint made after raking out about 1½" of mortar around the chimney.

Flashing must be installed so that no water can penetrate to the joint it is protecting. Roofing cement should be used and nails should be hammered in at the edges and joints. When roofing materials or shingles are used to cover the flashing, a coat of cement should be spread on the flashing.

Sometimes two flashings, or counter-flashing, are used wherein one metal strip overlaps another in much the same way that shingles are overlapped. Counter-flashing is frequently used around the chimney.

Chimney Flashing

When flashing is applied around the chimney it is necessary to rake out the mortar about 1½ inch. The edge of the flashing should be forced into the joint. Fresh mortar is then applied to the joint so that the flashing is firmly sealed in. Sometimes oakum is soaked with roofing cement

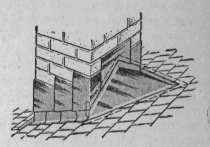

Fig. 6. The installation of a "cricket" or "saddle" between the back face of the chimney and the roof deck helps check the onrush of water.

and caulked into the joint to seal the folded metal in more securely. The flashing is continued down the chimney wall and bent to confirm with the angle made where chimney and roof surfaces meet. The lower part of the flashing is then extended under the roof shingles, thereby protecting the joint made between the front face of the chimney and the roof. Flashing is then extended completely around the chimney so that all the joints are sealed.

When the chimney is situated on a sloping roof, the rear portion of the chimney is likely to have water flow against it with considerable force. Then, too, the joint forms a neat little groove where snow and ice may accumulate. Consequently, the flashing protecting this particular juncture will have an abnormal amount of exposure. Leakage at this point is common. To reduce the force of the onrushing water so that the impact of the flow will not be so powerful, install what is known as a cricket, or saddle, between the back face of the chimney and the roof deck. The device is simply an inverted V-shaped wood framework which extends from the center line of the chimney back to the roof deck. It is flashed to the sloping roof in the back of the chimney. As the water comes pouring down the roof, it strikes this barrier and is divided. Its force is spent and it runs off on both sides of the chimney.

The location of chimneys on buildings may vary considerably. Where one is built on a separate foundation it is likely to have its own characteristics of settling and movement. Thus, flashings, protecting joints where the chimney meets the roof, must be able to allow for such movement without exposing the joints to water penetration.

Valley Flashing

When two roof surfaces come together at an angle they form what is known as a valley. The joint where they meet is always covered with flashing before the roof covering is applied. This protection is important because valleys are often part of the roof drainage system and large amounts of water frequently flow over them. Flashing waterproofs the

joint and prevents penetration, even during heavy storms.

When valley flashing is made too narrow, water is sometimes able to penetrate between the flashing and the roofing. This usually occurs when water has backed up in the valley because ice and snow were not properly drained off. This is a form of hydrostatic pressure, and it will force

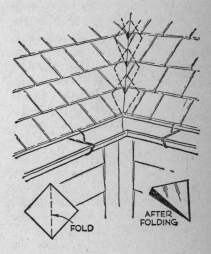

Fig. 7. Corroded flashing in the valley of the roof should be promptly repaired with small flat pieces of aluminum, tin, or galvanized sheet. Then fold and place as shown.

the water to run under the shingles. If the flashing beneath the shingles does not cover the area where the water gets through, therefore, leakage will take place through the unprotected portion.

When the flashings used in the valley become corroded so that they are no longer able to prevent water from getting through the roof they should be promptly repaired. Small flat pieces of aluminum, tin, galvanized sheet steel or copper are slid underneath the shingles to provide a more or less permanent solution. These pieces are generally 10-inch squares. They are folded in half so they form two triangles. Coat both sides with a roofing cement compound and then slide the piece carefully under the shingles and above the old flashing at the spot where the leakage occurred. Start at the lower course. Insert the pieces so that the sharp points on either end of the triangle are pushed up under the shingles on each side of the valley joint. The middle point should be pointing in the direction of the ground. The lower portion of each repair strip should be laid so that it overlaps the one beneath it. Usually these pieces are slipped under without any interference from nails. If some of the old nails do get in the way, however, use a long, slender cold chisel, a shingle hook, or a nail ripper to cut them away. After the job has been completed, new nails should be applied. Be certain that the original square piece of material which is inserted is large enough so that the overlaps will be as wide as the original flashing.

Dormer Flashing

When dormer windows are built, flashing between the roof and the side, or between the wall and roof, is installed so that it extends up under the siding and out over the shingles. This should be done so that a series of overlapping sheets are effected. If the siding is already in place, the flashing must be bent so that it can be shoved up under the siding. As soon as the flashing is installed, shingles are laid over it. It is a good idea for flashing to overlap the shingles so that a watertight joint between the meeting surfaces will be provided. If flashing has been omitted where the sill of a dormer window rests on a roof, it should be installed so that it may be worked into the underside of the sill and run down into the roofing material. Care must be taken in applying the flashing so that no water will get into the crevice between the sill and the roofing. As an added precaution, it is sometimes advisable to caulk the crack with roofing cement before applying the flashing.

Vent Pipe Flashing

Where pipes or ventilators, sometimes called soil stacks, project through the roof, the joints formed with the roof must be properly sealed with flashing to keep rain water from seeping through. This is usually accomplished by taking a piece of non-corrosive metal flashing, such as aluminum, and fitting it snugly over the vent and under the shingles. When the hole is cut in the flashing, the metal piece should be large enough to extend 4 inches below the pipe, 8 inches above it, and 6 inches on each side. Careful measurements should be made so that the hole will not be too large. After the metal piece is placed over the pipe, plastic cement is applied to provide a kind of collar and make the flashing fit tightly around the pipe. The cement must be made to adhere properly, thus it should be vigorously and thoroughly trowelled in place. It is then extended up the pipe and out over the flashing, at least 2 inches both ways. Shingles are finally laid over the flashing and formed around the pipe. Use plastic cement to secure the shingles. Nails should not be applied close to the pipe. The lower part of the flashing should lap over the shingles to provide a tighter seal.

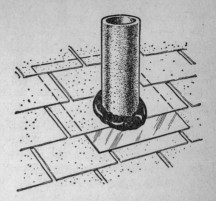

Fig. 8. The joint between the roof and the pipe is covered by flashing and then made fast with a collar of plastic cement.

Skylights

The joint between the roof and the skylight frame is also covered by flashing in about the same manner as the dormer flashing. Make certain that the flashing is secured to the frame. If there are any exposed holes or nail heads, these should be covered with roofing cement. The windows should be kept tight in the frame and, where putty has become dried out, it should be replaced. Where aluminum skylights are used, the best method of sealing glass to aluminum is with neoprene rubber.

REPAIRING OR REPLACING SHINGLES

Where shingles are worn out or damaged they should be repaired or replaced as soon as discovered. If not, the damage is very likely to spread and become more serious.

Asphalt Shingles

This type is generally conceded to be the most economical in use today. Asphalt shingles usually come in the form of two- or three-tab single strips. To repair these, the entire strip containing the damaged shingle must be removed and replaced. When asphalt shingles are damaged by strong winds, they will be raised and the surface beneath will be exposed to water penetration. This frequently happens to shingles in the four or five courses nearest the ridge, as well as those in the area which extends about 5 feet from the edge of the roof. To repair these shingles place a single blob of plastic, or quick-setting asphalt cement, on the surface of the underlying shingle roughly at the center of where the raised shingle tab will rest. Use only a small amount of plastic cement, about 1½ inches or the size of a half dollar. It may be applied with a putty knife, trowel or caulking gun. Press the tabs down firmly against the cement. Be careful to avoid squeezing it out over exposed surfaces. If too much plastic cement is used it may not be possible to make the shingle tabs lie flat at. Therefore, the lower edges of the tab should not be completely sealed. This method of sealing down the butts of the shingles in these areas is usually sufficient to repair shingles that have been yanked up by the wind. Where the wind is a continuing hazard it may be advisable to cement down the shingle tabs over the entire expanse of the roof.

Wood Shingles

These are frequently used on the roof because they are easily obtained. When wood shingles crack they can be temporarily repaired by inserting two 3″ x 8″ strips of galvanized tin or aluminum under the shingle. One sheet is driven up under the split shingle until its lower edge is flush with the edge of the shingle. The second strip is inserted so that it overlaps the first one and completely hides the crack caused by the split shingle. If it is difficult to get the metal strips started, pry up the lower edges of the wood shingle a trifle with a chisel, being careful not to cause additional damage to the shingle.

The most effective means of preventing leakage when a cracked wood shingle is spotted, however, is to remove and replace the shingle. Take a hatchet or a chisel and split the shingle into small bits. Remove the pieces and then with a hack saw blade, or metal cutting saw, cut off the tops of the two old shingle nails which were under the shingles above the one removed.

Once the new shingle has been fitted into place it should be fastened with ordinary nails driven down through the space between the two adjoining shingles above it. Be certain to align the joints between shingles. As a further precaution, the nail head may be covered with a strip of tin or aluminum inserted under the shingle above. This will prevent any possibility of rain leaking through the nail hole. Repairs to most other types of shingles are made in much the same way.

Asbestos Cement Shingles

These shingles are in common use, especially because of their fireproof and non-fading characteristics. When an asbestos shingle is broken it should be removed and replaced. To accomplish this, take out the old nails with a nail ripper and insert a new shingle by fastening nails through the vertical joint between the shingles and the overlying course above. Then insert a piece of sheet aluminum, or tin about 3″ x 8″ under the course above the nail head. This should extend about 2 inches under the course above, cover the nail, and extend 2 inches below it. Bend the metal slightly before insertion, in order that it will be held firmly in place.

Tile Roofing

If a tile is broken it should be removed and replaced. Take out the nails with a nail ripper. Apply roofing cement and set in a new tile. (See method described above for asbestos cement shingles.)

Slate Roofing

This is a more expensive type of covering save where the house is situated near a quarry. Individual broken slates are replaced in the same manner as noted above for asbestos cement shingles. Where very old slates fail because the nails used to fasten them have rusted, the entire roof covering including the felt underlay material, must be removed and replaced.

Metal Roofings

Roofs with a slight slope are often built of metals which provide a strong and permanent roofing. Where these metals are corrosion-resistant, such as aluminum, no painting or maintenance is required. Other materials used are galvanized iron, tin, copper, monel metal and zinc. Drops of solder may be used to fill small holes which may occur in metal roofs. If a large hole develops, it should be covered over with a piece of the same metal as the existing roof. This piece should also be attached with solder. Before joining the metal patch to the roof, however, both surfaces should be cleaned with a sharp tool, or rubbed with emery cloth until the metal is bright. Then apply an acid flux to the roof metal and the patching piece. A thin coating of solder should be used on each. Use a large soldering iron so that enough heat will be transmitted to the material to cause the solder to flow between the patching piece and the roof material. Be careful not to apply any more solder than is necessary.

RE-ROOFING

If the old roofing is badly worn out and causing leaks through the roof, steps must be taken to remedy the situation. It may not be necessary to remove the old roof, however, for many types of roofing can be applied directly over old wood shingles or other coverings. This method avoids the necessity of removing the old material and reduces the amount of cleaning necessary after such work is done. In addition, the old roof will provide extra insulation and, in the event of rain while re-roofing, the interior of the house will still be protected.

Before commencing re-roofing, any missing or badly broken shingles on the old roof should be replaced. If this is not possible, their places should be filled in so the new covering can be properly supported. Any shingles that are loose, warped or curled must be nailed securely in

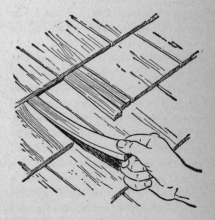

Fig. 9. Remove old shingles after cracking with a chisel and pulling out small pieces.

place. Check all nails to make certain they are driven down flush with the surface. Where new nails are added, they should be covered with roofing cement. The sheathing at eaves and edges should be examined. Boards which might be split by nails for the new roofing should be repaired or replaced. If the new roof creates open valleys which are so deep that they may retain ice and snow, they should be built up with a strip of roll roofing, asphalt shingle roofing, or wood shingle roofing. Before putting on new asphalt shingles, coat all the old surface with roofing cement.

The roofing must be pressed down flat so use a sharp knife to slit any puffs or large wrinkles in roll roofing. Then work cement underneath. Replace all old wood strips, which hold roll roofing at eaves and edges, with new ones.

NAILS

Many roofing failures are caused by the deterioration of nails. When they rust or break off, the roof covering becomes loose. This creates pockets which cause added pressure on the roofing material. Thus rust-resistant roofing nails are highly desirable for roof surfaces. In recent years, aluminum nails have come into increasingly wide use. These have a multitude of uses and can be used to fasten most roofing materials. When used in conjunction with metal roofing, such as corrugated aluminum roofing sheet, they are

equipped with a neoprene rubber washer to seat the nail, allow for expansion and contraction of the metal, and plug the hole that the nail makes. Nails used to fasten metal roofs should be of the same or similar metal as the roofing material.

CAPPING THE CHIMNEY

Occasionally rain water enters the house either directly through the chimney, or it penetrates the masonry joints of the chimney and leaks down through the inside walls. Chimneys must, therefore, be of watertight construction with some means of preventing water from falling directly into the flue.

Rain can be kept out of a chimney through the use of a hood. These hood openings should be at least equal in size to the area of the flue, and each flue should have a separate hood. It is also a good idea to project the flue lining about 4 inches above the cap or top course of brick, surrounding it with at least 2 inches of cement mortar. This should be finished with a straight or concave slope so that air currents will be directed upwards at the top of the flue. The sloped mortar also helps to drain water from the top of the chimney. Concrete and brick caps are usually made 4 inches thick, thus if these are projected an inch or two, a drip ledge will be formed which will provide an additional means of keeping the water out of the chimney.

INSTALLING A TV ANTENNA

Whenever anything is installed on a roof there is danger that the nails may cause holes which will lead to leakage. Considerable damage can be done to a roof, for example, if a television antenna is not carefully installed. The latter should not be attached to a chimney that has loose bricks or cracks in the mortar. Masonry must be in good condition before the added weight and strain of an antenna is put on it. It is important to select the proper size and style of bracket to fit your particular roof. If chimney straps are used, the brick and mortar can be protected by corner guards. Those with pipe clamps can be used, but the straps should be chosen and put on carefully.

If the strap is too narrow, it may cut into the mortar, damage the chimney and leave a wobbly antenna. On the other hand, a strap that is too thin should not be trusted for it might snap and drop the mast. Do not use improvised straps as they are not reliable. Galvanized steel straps about 1 inch wide are usually satisfactory.

When attaching an antenna, such as one with a few arms on a short mast, to brick walls or roof parapets, screw U clamps or stand-off brackets into the brick. Make the holes with a star drill and insert lead anchors to fasten the screws. If the mast extends down the wall for about 3 feet, at least two of these brackets are needed; if it extends down the

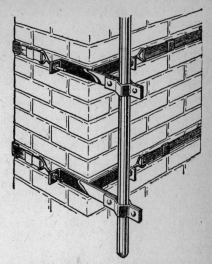

Fig. 10. TV antennas can be firmly attached by using chimney straps.

wall farther than this, the rule is to use a bracket every 3 feet.

A small antenna can be attached to the face of the gable end of a wood-sheathed house. Be sure the brackets are placed close to the pinnacle, and attached firmly to the wood. You can use log screws or even ordinary wood screws, although expansion or toggle bolts are recommended.

ROOF DRAINAGE SYSTEM

The roof drainage system has an important bearing on dampness and leakage inside the house. If water coming down from the roof is not diverted away from the sides of the foundation wall it may cause a serious water condition in the floors below. Moreover, if the roof drainage system is not kept operating properly, hydrostatic pressure may be caused by water backing up on the roof. This will cause leakage through the roof covering. Thus it is extremely important that gutters and downspouts (leaders) be kept open and in good repair at all times.

These drainage outlets should be thoroughly inspected at least twice a year. It is a good idea to make one inspection before the heavy spring rains, and another between the time when the leaves drop from the trees in the fall and the arrival of snow. Wherever a water condition develops inside the house, it is always a good idea to check the drainage system.

The most common type of drainage failure is caused by clogging due to leaves and other debris. This clogging will also cause the gutters to lose some of their pitch. A proper pitch is essential for water to run into the downspouts.

Check the gutter's pitch regularly. Empty a can of water in and ob-

Fig. 11. Empty a can of water into a roof gutter to check the pitch.

serve the way it drains off. It should drain away very quickly. If it does not, repair work is needed. Make certain there are no pockets where the water might collect. Also check on rusting, and see that leaves and debris are removed.

Gutters are made either half-round or molded. Downspouts are either round or rectangular. A gutter should be installed at the eave of every roof that sheds water, and at least one downspout should be applied for every run of gutter. A downspout should be installed at each corner of the house, and each should drain not more than 20 feet of gutter on each side of the spout.

Sagging Gutters

Very often a wood gutter that has sagged and lost its pitch can be repaired simply by forcing it back into position. If there is a molding, it should first be removed. Following this, apply pressure with a heavy hammer to force the gutter back into position. Use a block of wood to prevent damage to the trough. If old nails interfere with the return of the trough to its proper position, they should be removed with a cold chisel. Re-nail the gutter with eight or ten-penny nails, and replace the molding. All nails and putty holes should be filled. Touch up unpainted spots and repaint the gutter, as a whole. Use asphalt paint in the trough and house paint on the underside.

Sagging metal gutters can often be corrected by merely bending hangars up or down slightly, as required. Sometimes extra hangers can be installed to prevent future sagging. If there is a bad buckle or fold, remove the gutter. Hammer out the crease with a soft-faced hammer, using a block of wood or metal shaped similar to the gutter to protect it. Soft-faced hammers come with heads of wood fiber or plastic. They will not damage the metal surface. Avoid using a ball-peen hammer as it will mar the appearance of the gutter.

If the gutter is completely enclosed above the wall, in box-like fashion, it can only sag at the edge. In this case, the first thing to do is to remove the trim. Secondly, loosen the outer edge of the metal lining, if necessary, and reinforce or replace the exposed supporting frame. When you finish repairing the gutter, be certain that it is lined up properly so that it will drain into the downspout. The trim is then replaced and the metal lining refastened at the edge as it was originally.

Removing Rust

When a gutter is badly rusted it will leak. If the metal is very thin it may not be possible to remove the rust without making holes. In this case, replace the gutter. Where it is possible to make a repair, however, the first thing to do is to scrape out as much rust as you can. To do this, use a wire brush or coarse steel wool, and scrape away the rust from the bottom side of the gutter as well. The inside of the rusty gutter is then coated with a good grade of asphaltum paint. It may be thinned

or diluted with an equal part of white (unleaded) gasoline so that brushing will be easier. The asphaltum should be allowed to dry before continuing the job. Once it is dry, coat it with a thick film of plastic cement. Use a waterproof type especially prepared for roof and gutter repairs, and spread a ⅛″ film covering. Then apply strips of heavy aluminum foil over the surface of the gutter before the waterproof cement sets. The foil should be pressed down tightly with a dry cloth. Where the strips of foil come together they should be overlapped in the direction of the water flow. Finally, cement the edges together.

Preventing Clogging

When clogging occurs, it is often due to wet leaves in an elbow. Re-

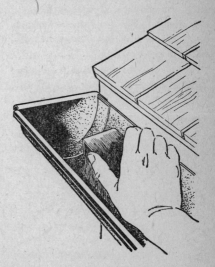

Fig. 12. Prior to making repairs in roof gutters, scrape out rust. Then coat with a good grade of asphaltum paint.

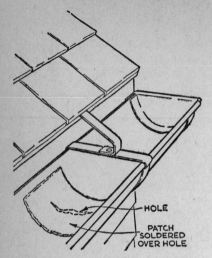

HOLE

PATCH
SOLDERED
OVER HOLE

Fig. 13. Patch small holes in gutters with pieces of metal fastened to the lining by soldering around the edges.

move the elbow and clean it. If you try to force the leaves down you may cause a worse clogging condition in the downspout. To keep leaves out of gutters, buy some chicken wire at the hardware store, fasten it to the roof onto the first row of shingles, and then hook it over the gutter's edge. While this will work well in keeping leaves out of the gutter such an arrangement may contribute to clogging up large amounts of snow and ice during the winter.

Patching Gutters

Small holes in gutters are repaired by soldering. When the gutter is made of aluminum, care should be exercised in selecting the proper solder. Larger openings, however, should be covered with pieces of metal, the same as the lining. These patches are laid over the hole and fastened to the lining by soldering around the edges. Another method of patching gutters is to spread a piece of asphalt roofing felt over the opening. This should first be fastened with roofing cement. Then, after it is laid and pressed smooth and tight, apply another coating of asphalt roofing cement, or putty, with a trowel on top of the felt. This method is especially handy as a temporary means of repairing holes during the winter when soldering is usually difficult or impossible. Sometimes small holes are merely plugged by a dab of paint and asphalt cement.

Repairing Downspouts

In general, downspouts are repaired in the same manner outlined for gutters. Where a bad deficiency exists, the section should be replaced.

REMOVING ICE AND SNOW

Ice and snow will cause water to back up on the roof itself, or overflow against the foundation walls. After a heavy snowfall has fallen, it is a good idea to scrape away the snow at least 4 feet back from the eaves. Also shovel out valleys. Do not use salt to melt snow where aluminum, which reacts unfavorably to salt, is used.

A heating cable, or an electric deicing coil, can be laid in gutters. These devices will melt the snow before it has a chance to accumulate. The coil is simply laid the length of the gutter, and when ice forms the plug is inserted in an electric outlet. The heat rapidly melts any ice or snow.

A freeze-back or metal flashing can also be installed on the edge of roofs where extreme snow and icy conditions prevail. An aluminum metal freeze-back conducts the heat from the interior of the house to the edge of the roof, which is normally an overhang, and thus the same temperature as the outside. Even where houses are insulated there is more heat loss 2 feet up the roof, than there is right at the edge of the roof. In addition, the aluminum sheet metal presents a very smooth surface so that snow and ice are not as likely to form on it and build up. It is recommended that a sheet metal man or roofer apply this type of construction, inasmuch as this is a type of standing seam roof and requires special tools for forming.

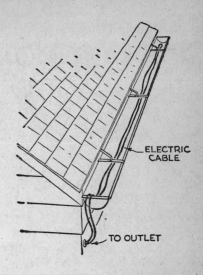

ELECTRIC CABLE

TO OUTLET

Fig. 14. A device designed to melt snow in gutters is this electric de-icing coil, which is simply plugged in as soon as snow accumulates.

CHAPTER 12

THE BATHROOM AND KITCHEN; THE ATTIC

Water is frequently spilled on bathroom and kitchen floors. Unless these surfaces are carefully constructed, leakage will occur in rooms below. Usually the bathroom and kitchen floors are made waterproof when they are built. When additional bathrooms are built or when there is excessive spillage on the kitchen floor, good waterproofing practices should be followed.

THE BATHROOM

Water conditions develop in a bathroom due to spilling from overflowing tubs or washstands and to drips from leaky pipes or showers whose streams pour against the wall or spill on the floor. Condensation also occurs on bathroom windows and cold surfaces. *See Chapter 5 on Condensation.*

Bathroom Floors

A bathroom floor must be able to hold any water which spills on it and prevent it from flowing through to a ceiling or wall below. Thus most modern bathrooms have floors which are made waterproof at the time of construction. This is usually done with a prepared waterproof plaster made of white gypsum, or some light plaster that contains no portland cement. One of the most popular plasters is known as Keene's cement. This is applied under the tile finish. It is also possible to use a portland cement plaster with an integral waterproofing compound. This mixture can be made at home and is much cheaper than Keene's cement. It also provides a lot more structural strength, but it is not nearly as ornate.

Floors made in this manner will prevent water due to spillage from causing damage to surfaces in rooms below. It is important, to smear-proof plaster all around the holes through which pipes enter the bathroom. Moreover, if the washstand and toilet are of the pedestal type, they should be set in a waterproof mortar. The latter is usually white or gray in color, and serves to seal the joint between the porcelain and the floor. The joints between the bathtub and the floor should also be sealed with mortar.

Dealing with the Shower

If windows are situated where water from the shower frequently sprays against them, they may be damaged unless protected. Waterproof curtains should be installed.

234

These come in a variety of decorative styles and colors and will protect the wood or metal surfaces from deterioration. Where a new shower is being installed it should be kept as far away from the windows and walls as possible. Even if the water does not strike the window surfaces directly, the steam may sometimes be sufficient to cause corrosion and rot the wood. Where the shower must be placed close to windows, always use protective hangings.

Walls near a shower are frequently soaked. The water saturates the surface and causes stains on the ceiling or walls below. Where a shower is encased in a glass enclosure this will not happen, thus this type of construction is highly recommended. In those instances where a shower is installed over a bathtub, however, waterproof curtains must be used to protect the wall and floor. The most effective method is to use two curtains hung on parallel rods running along either side of the tub. This provides very effective protection with the only possible damage resulting from steam.

If the shower is installed over the tub with a metal ring at the top from which the curtain hangs, it is advisable to place the opening of the curtain at the front of the shower, rather than at the back next to the wall. As a result, any splashing that occurs through the curtain opening then runs into the tub instead of pouring against the wall. however, the curtain should be pliable enough so that you can turn the faucet handles, or else a hole should be

made through which handles will pass.

The wall surface around the bathtub, or wherever shower water might strike, should be properly waterproofed. If it is not, the only thing to do is to fix up the entire wall or

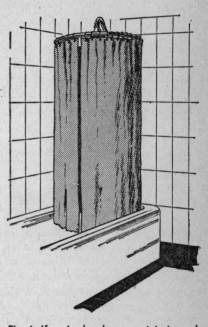

Fig. I. If a circular shower curtain is used, place the opening at the front, away from the wall.

provide a means for waterproofing the points where the water splashes. An oilcloth can be used to cover the wall, or some form of artificial tile may be attached with a black mastic plaster or a white plaster. Additional protection can be provided for the floor by spreading a rubber mat whenever the surface is likely to get wet. When not in use, the mat may be simply rolled up and stored in a closet or hung on the side of the tub.

When repairs are necessary at joints between the bathtub and the wall, they may be sealed with Keene's cement. This should be mixed with water to a consistency that can be applied with a trowel.

Fig. 2. The entrance to a shower should always have a sill.

For joint work of this kind use a pointed brickmason's trowel, rather than oblong plasterer's trowel. The trowel's point is used to scrape out the joint, force the plaster into it, and finish it off at the surface. Since this work is done in one coat, it must be done quickly because the cement sets up within a short time after it is put in place.

Installing A Shower or Bathroom

If you want to install an extra shower stall or bathroom, the floor must be waterproof. This may mean that the floor level will be a little higher in the new bathroom than it is in adjacent rooms on the same floor, but the additional waterproof flooring must be put in or spillage will cause damage to rooms below.

New floors can be waterproofed with portland cement, sand, and an integral waterproofer. This mixture is applied about 1 inch thick on top of the existing floor, or on top of the floor boards under the finished floor. If the finished floor has been put in, as it may be in any case except the attic. you can cut down to the sub-floor and the thickness of the cement can be made flush with the original floor level. Next, on top of your waterproofed cement floor you must install some kind of finished floor, which will probably be tile. This will still, therefore, make the new bathroom floor a little higher than floors on the same level.

Joints or openings made by pipes or fixtures must be carefully sealed. The bathtub, if there is one, should be set in plaster and sealed at the floor level. Where there is a shower, the wall should be protected, as discussed above, or waterproofed either with plaster or artificial or regular tile. This must be run up to a height which will protect the construction in back of the wall from any water which might pour or splash against it from the shower stream.

When a shower stall of any type is installed in the bathroom, the three walls of the stall are made watertight no matter what type of material is used in construction. Moreover, the entrance should always have a sill connecting the two side walls, so that the water cannot flow out from the stall on to the bathroom floor. If the stall is a glass enclosure, the sill can be of glass, too. If the stall is made of some opaque material, such as slate, the sill can be similarly made of slate, or it can be built up with cement mortar.

THE KITCHEN

Spillage from sinks and washing machines and leakage from corroded pipes are the chief cause of a water condition in the kitchen. When large amounts of water get on the kitchen floor there is always danger that the surfaces of rooms below may become stained and furnishings soiled. If the kitchen is situated above a basement storeroom, for example, the contents of the room may be ruined if water gets through, and there will be damage to the floor boards and walls.

Waterproof Kitchen Floors

It is advisable to have a floor cover which will hold the water and not let it get through to the boards or basement underneath. Housewives generally prefer linoleum for this purpose, because a tile floor takes a heavy toll in breakage when things drop. A good linoleum can be properly laid with a commercial mastic binder. These are made specifically for sealing linoleum to paper underneath. They are of a fluid nature and can be applied with a brush. The paper is fibrous and is especially designed for laying under linoleum. It comes in rolls.

When linoleum is to be run right up to the wall, the bead and baseboard around the wall are removed. It is a good idea to cut the paper a little bit full so that the edge can be turned up at the wall to form a tight seal between the floor and wall. This gives added protection if any water gets over as far as that joint, in

Fig. 3. Water dripping through a kitchen floor may damage more than you think.

which case it is not so likely to get into the woodwork and rot it.

Openings where pipes come through the walls are especially vulnerable to water penetration. These holes are generally covered only with a piece of round metal which fits around the pipe loosely. Water may seep through quite easily. The best way to close up these holes is to fill them with putty or any soft wood sealer which is pliable enough to be forced into the irregular opening between the floor and the pipe.

Care should be taken in the kitchen to prevent spillage. However, automatic appliances, such as dishwashing machines, are prone to overflow every now and then. While the faulty machine may be fixed, it is advisable to have additional precautions to prevent the water from going through the floor. Thus, if you are building or remodeling a kitchen, a cement floor topping should be laid right over the wood, and it should have a base around the walls so the cement can be carried up about 6 or 8 inches on the side. In this way, you get a watertight pan for a floor in the kitchen. When spillage occurs, the water will simply be held within the confines of the kitchen where it can be wiped or soaked up and no damage will result to anything that may be stored below in the basement or to the woodwork of the flooring itself.

THE ATTIC

Water problems connected with the attic depend on the type of construction and how the space is utilized. If, for example, you have an unfinished attic used principally as a storeroom, any water penetration will damage the furnishings and other possessions stored there. The problems, though will be the same as those that apply to the rest of the superstructure. Vulnerable points are at mortar joints, openings in walls, or the roof. Where no windows exist, condensation may occur. (See Ventilating the Attic in Chapter 5).

Louvers

Unfinished attics are frequently ventilated by means of louvers. These are small openings constructed primarily for ventilating purposes. As they must be kept open at all times, it is necessary to build them so that air may come in but rain and snow are kept out. The slits are usually tilted to achieve this condition. Where rain does come through, a visor is sometimes put over the window, although it is better to extend the louvers so that the overlap or tilt is greater. Louvers are installed as a unit. A rustproof metal, such as aluminum, is recommended, for it will prevent streaking of light-surfaced buildings and reduce maintenance costs.

Finished Attics

When the attic space is to be used either for a play room or living quarters, great care must be taken to avoid introducing water conditions into the house. New partitions or finished surfaces must be built without interfering with the watertightness of the walls or the roof. In addition, when windows and exhaust fans are installed, such installations break the continuity of construction and caulking and flashing must be provided to prevent leakage at the joints.

If a bathroom or shower is installed in the attic, provisions must also be made to prevent any spillage or plumbing leakage from penetrating to the floors below. If an inexpensive job is desired, oilcloth may be put on the bathroom or shower wall instead of tile, and the floor under the shower section may be made of waterproof cement or a waterproof cement mortar instead of tile.

An attic kitchen requires precautions, too. Again oilcloth could be satisfactorily substituted for linoleum on the floor, although the latter is sturdier.

Fig. 4. Construction and protection of louvers. Louvers should always be kept open.

INDEX